WORLD
OF
READING

SKILLS PRACTICE

SILVER SECRETS

LEVEL 10

SILVER BURDETT & GINN

NEEDHAM, MA • MORRISTOWN, NJ
ATLANTA, GA • CINCINNATI, OH • DALLAS, TX
MENLO PARK, CA • NORTHFIELD, IL

◆ CONTENTS ◆

ISBN 0-663-47835-9

Story Mapping

A story map shows the important parts of a story. The **beginning** gives the setting. The **middle** tells the *problem*. The **ending** gives the *solution* to the problem.

Read the story about Minerva Squirrel. Then complete the story map.

It was a beautiful spring day. Minerva Squirrel had finished exploring and eating. She was ready to return home to her big tree, which was on a spot of land that curved out from the edge of the lake.

When she arrived there, however, Minerva found trouble. Two beavers were building a dam. Their dam made a little pond that cut Minerva's tree off from the land.

Minerva asked the beavers if they would stop building the dam. They said they were sorry, but they needed the dam and the little pond. Then Minerva talked to her cousin, Red-Tail. He said that it was no trouble to fly back and forth from a tree on land to the big tree. But, alas, Minerva could not fly. Finally, Minerva had an idea. She asked the beavers to do her a favor.

In no time at all, the beavers felled a small tree. It made a nice bridge across the little pond to Minerva's tree. Minerva was happy. She had not lost her home, and she had new friends.

Who:
Where:
When:

Problem:

EVENTS LEADING TO RESOLUTION

Resolution:

Inference

Every detail about a character or a situation is not always stated directly in a story. Often a reader must use clues given in the story and use personal experience to figure out the details that are not explained directly in the story. This is called **making inferences.**

Story Clues
+ Experience Clues
Inference

Read the story. Write answers to the questions.

To make inferences from a story, do two things:
1. Search for clues in the story.   2. Use ideas from your own experience.

Sachi closed the book. Then she put the book in her lap and sank back into the chair.

1. What had Sachi just finished doing?

_____

Sachi fell asleep in the chair. She dreamed of the adventures of the main character, Carol Carson. She dreamed of herself helping the girl detective solve the mysteries.

2. How did Sachi feel about the character Carol Carson?

_____

_____

Sachi woke up with a jolt. The book was on the floor. The room was quiet and cozy.

3. What noise had woken Sachi?

_____

Suddenly Sachi had an idea. She ran to the telephone and called her friend Amy. When Amy answered, Sachi asked, ''Do you have any more Carol Carson books?''

4. Why did Sachi want to know if Amy had any more Carol Carson books?

_____

_____

Vocabulary: Story Critical Words

A. Study the meaning of each word.

aliens imaginary beings from outer space	**permission** consent
colonize to start a colony or settlement	**residence** one's home
culture the way of life of a group of people	**robot** a machine to do some human jobs
developments happenings, events	**settlement** a small village

B. Lisa is a news reporter living on the planet Stexar. She sends the following report to Earth. Unfortunately, some words are missing. Read the report. Finish each incomplete sentence with the correct vocabulary word.

NEWS FROM THE PLANET STEXAR

A spaceship of _____ from a faraway planet landed here today. The traffic _____ who made first contact with them discovered that they were friendly. They asked for _____ to meet with Stexar's president. They were led to Crystal House, the official _____ of President Zalar. The visitors told the president that they would like to start a _____ on Stexar. They told the president that they thought each could learn a lot from the other's _____ . President Zalar liked that idea, so she told them that they could _____ an uninhabited part of the planet.

C. Sometimes the meaning of a word is given in a clue. Read each sentence clue. Then write the correct word.

1. Early groups of people who came to America from Europe lived together in this.

_____

2. Sometimes you need to ask for this to do something. _____

3. This can include the art and music that a group of people make.

_____

4. These are things that happen in time. _____

Vocabulary: Support Words

A. Study the meaning of each word.

disintegrated broken into parts
hostile warlike; unfriendly
immigration the act of coming into a foreign land to live
miniature very small

miscalculated figured or planned wrongly
naturalization the act of making a citizen of
stranded left in a difficult situation
tribute something done to show respect

B. Finish each sentence with the correct vocabulary word.

1. Someone who likes airplanes might collect _____ models of them.

2. Someone who is _____ on a highway might wave at a passing car for help.

3. Someone who _____ a math problem would get a wrong answer.

4. Someone who is treated unfairly might become _____.

5. Someone who does many good deeds for a community might receive a

   _____.

C. Answer each question with vocabulary words.

6. Which two words could refer to a person moving to a foreign country?

   _____   _____

7. How might you describe a plate that was smashed on the ground?

   _____

8. How might an enemy act? _____

D. Synonyms are words that have almost the same meanings. Write the vocabulary word that is a synonym for each underlined word.

9. The old skipper liked to carve <u>tiny</u> ships. _____

10. The delicate vase <u>shattered</u> when the cat accidentally knocked it over.

   _____

Telephone Directory

The **yellow pages** is the classified section of the telephone directory. In the yellow pages, advertisers are listed alphabetically by type of business or service offered.

A. Look at the sample page from the yellow pages. Use the information on the sample page to fill in the circle next to the best answer to each question.

Skate Sharpening

Cutting Edge, The
    Skate sharpening & repairs
    655 Lacey Terr., Gardner 555-8971

Skating Equipment & Supplies

Ice Palace, The
    Sales only, no rentals
    All name-brand merchandise
    1200 Mystic Rd., Newtowne 555-1400

Midland Skate Shop   *Sales & rentals*
    Hockey, dance, freestyle
    521 Lakeside Dr., Gardner 555-4549

Skating Instruction

Sonya's Ice Skating Studio
    Children & adult classes
    Beginners through advanced
    170 Edison St., Gleason 555-9500

Peterson's Skating School
    Specializing in ice dancing
    10 Hobson Ave., Gardner 555-5641

Skating Rinks—Ice

Tri-Town Skating Rink   Public and team skating
    Open all year
    1511 Main St., Gardner 555-8731

---

1. Under what letter in the directory would you find information on skating?

(a) M for Midland   (c) R for Rinks

(b) E for Equipment   (d) S for Skating

2. Which heading tells you where you can learn how to skate?

(a) Skating Rinks—Ice   (c) Skate Sharpening

(b) Skating Equipment & Supplies   (d) Skating Instruction

3. Which place would you call to rent a pair of skates?

(a) The Ice Palace   (c) Midland Skate Shop

(b) Sonya's Ice Skating Studio   (d) The Cutting Edge

B. On separate paper, list two other kinds of information you can find about skating from this sample directory.

Inference

Sometimes we know more things about a story than just the things the story says. Read the example.

Example: Lora trudged on, shaking the damp hair out of her eyes. Then she shivered as water began to seep into her shoes.

Story Clues
+	Experience Clues
Inference

You know that Lora is cold and wet from passage clues in the example and from your own experience.

Read the rest of the story. Answer the questions about the story.

> Lora pulled her thin cotton jacket tightly around her. Then she tried to make herself warm by thinking about a cozy fireplace. Just then, Mrs. Lopez pulled up in her car. She took one look at her soaking wet neighbor and said, "Goodness, Lora, you look as if you could use a ride home!"
>
> After Lora closed the door, she laid her head against the seat and thanked Mrs. Lopez. Then Lora began to tell her how she had ended up in that soggy situation.

1. Had Lora expected bad weather that day? How do you know?

_____

_____

2. Did Lora and Mrs. Lopez know each other? How do you know?

_____

_____

3. How does Laura feel about Mrs. Lopez's offer? How do you know?

_____

4. Where was Lora at the end of the story?

_____

5. Underline the parts of the story that gave you clues for answering question 3.

Classification

Classifying means putting things into groups. A word map classifies, or groups, words that are related. Look at the example. Find the two words in the box that are related to the heading *Thanksgiving*. Add them to the word map part.

autumn · corn · Thanksgiving · Pilgrims · pie

Example: **Thanksgiving**

corn _____

Pilgrims _____

_____

_____

fireworks
flags
Native Americans
turkey

Did you add ''Native Americans'' and ''turkey''? If you did, you understand how to group words in a word map.

Use the words in the box to complete this word map for *Books*.

1. Sources of books

_____

_____

_____

_____

3. Places to store books

_____

_____

_____

_____

Books

2. Subjects in school books

_____

_____

_____

4. Parts of some books

_____

_____

_____

book bag
bookcase
bookstore
chapters
contents
desk
English
friends
glossary
index
library
locker
math
school
science
spelling

Do all of the words in each group relate to its heading?

NAME _____

SKILLS PRACTICE   **8**

Prefixes *in-*, *mis-*, *non-*

A **prefix** is a word part added to the beginning of a word. It changes the meaning of the word. The word parts *mis-*, *in-*, and *non-* are prefixes. Knowing the meanings of prefixes will help you figure out the meanings of unfamiliar words. Study these prefixes.

Prefixes	Meanings	Sample Words
in-	"not", "in"	incorrect
mis-	"bad", "wrong", "not"	misunderstood
non-	"not", "the reverse of", "the absence of"	nonpayment

Read the sentences. Add the prefix to the underlined word, and write the new word.

1. *in-*   The children are usually very <u>active</u>. When it started to rain, however, they had to come inside and be _____ .

2. *non-*   Inside, they had to <u>stop</u> running around. Outside, they had been able to run _____ .

3. *in-*   The children looked sadly at the closed <u>door</u>. Then they started to play _____ games.

4. *in-*   Nora was <u>direct</u> when she asked some classmates for help. She was usually more _____ .

5. *mis-*   Nora asked Les to <u>print</u> the names on the carnival invitations. She asked him not to _____ any of the names.

6. *mis-*   Les used the telephone book to <u>spell</u> each name correctly. He did not want to _____ even one.

7. *mis-*   The boys will try to <u>understand</u> the directions. But the more they try the more they seem to _____ them.

8. *in-*   I thought I had written the <u>correct</u> answers. When the papers were returned, I saw that two were _____ .

9. *non-*   They planned to make a <u>payment</u> today. They did not want to be called about _____ .

©:Silver, Burdett & Ginn Inc.

8   LEVEL 10   "Teeny, Tiny, Tinny Visitors"

Multiple Meanings

A **multiple meaning** word is a word that has more than one meaning. You can often figure out each meaning of a multiple meaning word by checking the words around it for clues. Some multiple meaning words are spelled the same but are pronounced differently and have different meanings. Notice how *lead* is used in the example.

> Example: Shaun will *lead* us in setting up scenery for the play.
>
> The tall cardboard trees are as heavy as *lead*.

A. Complete each sentence by using a word in two different ways.
Use the other words in the sentences as clues.

act	bow	clear	left	part	right	trip

1. Tess tried out for the _____ of the queen.

She took her time reading each difficult _____ of the script.

2. In the second _____ , the queen was lost in the forest.

Tess had to _____ frightened and confused.

3. The queen was the only one _____ on stage now.

Soon a tired looking elf entered from the _____ side of the stage.

4. Walking over to the queen, the elf started to _____ and fall.

The queen caught him and asked if he had been away on a _____ .

5. The elf pointed with his _____ hand to the painted mountains.

The queen was _____ in guessing that he was lost, too.

6. It was _____ from then on that the two would help each other.

They sat down next to a crystal _____ brook and made a plan.

7. Then, as they left, the queen fixed the fancy _____ on her gown.

After the curtain fell, the actors came on stage and took a _____ .

B. On separate paper, write the meaning and a rhyming word for each word you wrote in number 7.

Vocabulary: Story Critical Words

A. Study the meaning of each word.

circuits   wiring through which electricity
   flows

controller   a person or thing that controls

firm   a company

functional   in working order

gears   wheels with teeth that fit together

puppet   a figure moved by strings or hands

static   electric charges that cause crackling
   sounds

B. Read each paragraph. Finish each incomplete sentence
   with the correct vocabulary word.

   The mechanic oiled the _____ so that

the car would drive smoothly. He also checked the electrical

_____ . He said our car was _____ . But

when we turned on the radio, all we heard was _____ .

   My father works for the Funtoy Company. That _____ decided

to give a party for the employees' children. The _____ in charge of

the entertainment thought it would be fun to have a _____ show.

C. Write the vocabulary word each sentence tells about.

   1. This person makes sure that everything runs smoothly. _____

   2. This is a synonym for *business*. _____

   3. If something works as it should, it is this. _____

   4. This can look like a person or a creature and is used to entertain people.

   _____

D. One letter is missing from each word below. Look at each word carefully. On the line,
   write the missing letter. Then write the word correctly. The first one has been done
   for you.

   5. pupet _____ p, puppet _____

   6. funcional _____

   7. circuis _____

   8. gers _____

Vocabulary: Support Words

A. Study the meaning of each word.

electronics the science of devices that use electricity

nightmare a frightening dream

operative in operation

seethed bubbled or foamed

unmeshed pulled apart

B. Finish each sentence with the correct vocabulary word. Write the word in the puzzle.

Across

3. During the storm the waves _____ .

4. He was relieved to wake up from his _____ .

5. After I dropped my radio, it was no longer _____ .

Down

1. Because my sister is good at _____ , she could fix our television.

2. The machine made a loud noise as the gears were _____ .

C. Write the vocabulary word each sentence tells about.

6. Something that is working is this. _____

7. Radios and televisions are made by people who know this.

_____

8. The soda water did this when it was stirred. _____

Multiple Meanings

A **multiple meaning** word is a word that has more than one meaning. These two crossword puzzles use different meanings of the same words. Use one puzzle to help you complete the other.

Across

3 the inside part of the hand

4 a place to keep money

Down

1 an upper limb of the body

2 a weapon with a long, pointed blade

5 a young goat

Across

1 to stab or pierce

4 to furnish with weapons

5 to tease or fool

Down

2 a tree with a tall trunk and a bunch of large leaves at the top

3 the land at the sides of a river

Comparison

Writers may describe how people, events, things, and stories are alike or different through **comparisons.** Words like *same, both, alike, different, but,* and *whereas* often signal comparisons. Read the example to see how Fran and Sato are alike and how they are different.

> Example: Fran likes to play softball, whereas Sato prefers to
> play basketball. Both children like to use computers.

A. Read the following paragraph. Then write sentences to answer the questions.

Mike, Lily, and Tim all live on High Street. Lily and Tim have lived on High Street all their lives, but Mike moved there recently. This will be Mike's first year at Beecher School, whereas Lily and Tim have gone there for four years. Mike likes to play baseball. Lily and Tim could not tell him very much about baseball at school because Lily likes gymnastics, and Tim likes to play soccer. The three friends enjoy reading the same type of books. The type they all like best is mysteries.

1. How are Mike, Lily and Tim alike in where they live? _____

_____

2. How are Lily and Tim alike in where they go to school? _____

_____

3. How is Mike different from Lily and Tim in where he lives and goes to school?

_____

_____

4. How are Mike, Lily, and Tim different in what sports they like? _____

_____

5. How are Mike, Lily, and Tim alike in what they enjoy reading? _____

_____

B. Underline the words that signal comparisons in the paragraph. On separate paper, use each one in a new sentence.

Dictionary

A **dictionary** is made up of entry words listed in alphabetical order. Each entry tells how a word is pronounced and what the word means. Two guide words are printed at the top of each dictionary page.

A. Use the sample dictionary page to answer the questions.

---

circus/cite

cir·cus (sʉr′kəs) **n.** **1** a traveling show held in tents or in a hall, with clowns, trained animals, acrobats, etc. **2** a very funny or entertaining person or thing. **3** a stadium or arena in ancient Rome, where games or races were held.

PRONUNCIATION KEY

a	fat	ī	bite, fire	ou	out	zh	leisure
ā	ape	o	hop	u	up	ŋ	ring
ä	car, lot	ō	go	ur	fur		a *in* ago
e	ten	ô	law, horn	ch	chin		e *in* agent
er	care	oi	oil	sh	she	ə =	i *in* unity
ē	even	oo	look	th	thin		o *in* collect
i	hit	o͞o	tool	*th*	then		u *in* focus
ir	here						

cir·rus (sir′əs) **n.** a kind of cloud that looks like thin strips of woolly curls.

cit·a·del (sit′ə d'l) **n.** **1** a fort on a high place, for defending a town. **2** a place of safety.

ci·ta·tion (sī tā′shən) **n.** **1** an order to come to a law court. **2** a telling or quoting of something written in a book, article, etc. **3** an official mention that praises.

cite (sīt) **v.** **1** to order to come to a law court. **2** to mention or quote. **3** to mention for praise —**cit′ed, cit′ing**

---

1. What are the guide words on this page? _____

2. In this dictionary, would this page be near the beginning, in the middle, or near the end? _____

3. How many meanings are given for the word *circus*? _____

4. Which meaning of *citation* is used in this sentence? Ms. Yin was given a citation for bravery. _____

5. Which word means "a fort on a high place, for defending a town"? _____

B. From the dictionary page, choose a word that has more than one meaning. On separate paper, write a sentence for each meaning of the word.

"The Mad Puppet" and "Calvin and Hobbes"

Sequence

In stories, many things or events happen in a certain **order,** or **sequence.** As you read, look for words like *first*, *next*, *before*, *after*, *then*, *later*, *as*, and *while*. These are words that signal the time order of events. To check to see that you have the correct order, ask yourself: "Does the sequence make sense?"

Example: Sara put on her skates. Then she skated onto the ice. While Sara skated, she moved her arms for balance.

| Event | → | then | → | Event |

| Event | ← | while | → | Event |

Read the paragraph. Then write the events in the order in which they happened.

Trudy and Terri decided to clean their messy room. First, they straightened up their bookshelves and closets. As they sorted through a stack of old magazines, they threw some of them away. Next, the two girls packed many of their old toys and games into a large box. They carried the box to the Turn-Around Treasure Shop. After Trudy and Terri returned home, they dusted their room until it looked like new.

1 _____
_____

2 _____
_____

3 _____
_____

4 _____
_____

5 _____
_____

6 _____
_____

7 _____
_____

8 _____
_____

Do your sentences match the order of the events in the paragraph?

Vocabulary: Story Critical Words

A. Study the meaning of each word.

bargain something gotten cheaply
desperate reckless because one has
  lost hope
emergency a situation needing immediate
  attention

ordinary usual; regular
poultry fowl raised for food; chickens
refunds money returned
reserved set aside for later use
ungrateful not thankful

B. Sometimes the meaning of a word is given in a clue. Read each sentence clue. Then write the correct word.

1. This is an antonym for *unusual*. _____

2. A person who forgets to say thank you for a gift will appear to be this.

  _____

3. When a river floods a town, this might be declared. _____

4. This refers to a "good deal." _____

5. Customers returning products sometimes ask for these. _____

6. A person stranded in an unfamiliar place without any money might feel this way.

  _____

7. If you wanted to buy a Thanksgiving turkey, you might go to this section of the

  supermarket. _____

8. You might see a sign on a restaurant table saying this. _____

C. Complete each analogy by writing the correct vocabulary word.

9. *Apple* is to *fruit* as *chicken* is to _____.

10. *Short* is to *tall* as *thankful* is to _____.

11. *Happy* is to *sad* as *hopeful* is to _____.

12. *Empty* is to *full* as *unusual* is to _____.

13. *Event* is to *happening* as *deal* is to _____.

14. *Matches* is to *fire* as *accident* is to _____.

15. *Football* is to *kicked* as *tickets* is to _____.

Vocabulary: Support Words

A. Study the meaning of each word.

appointment   a date to meet someone at a certain time

banister   the railing on a staircase

numb   having lost feeling

suspected   guessed or supposed

tamely   gently

B. Each sentence tells about a vocabulary word. Write the word in the puzzle.

Across

3. You can make this to see someone.

5. This word has to do with trying to figure out something.

Down

1. This is how your fingers might feel if you don't wear gloves on a cold day.

2. You can lean against this.

4. This is an antonym for *wildly*.

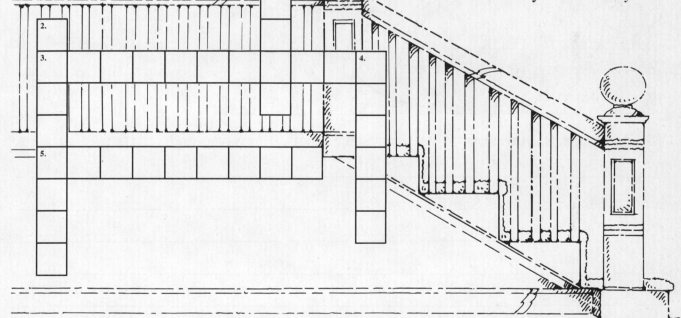

C. Finish each sentence with the correct vocabulary word.

6. Barry _____ that Ken was planning a surprise party for him.

7. The circus lion acted _____ with its trainer.

8. Jerry had an _____ to see his dentist.

9. The little girl held on to the _____ as she walked down the stairs.

Maps

This road map shows part of the Bay Area in California. A **road map** shows highways and roads and helps you travel from place to place.

A. Use the information on the map to answer the questions.

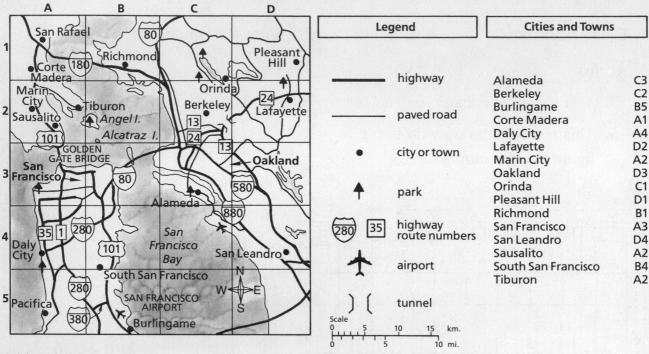

1. Which bridge do you cross to go from San Francisco to Sausalito? _____

_____

2. What cities are south of San Francisco? _____

_____

_____

_____

3. Where, according to the grid, is the tunnel? _____

4. Where is San Rafael on the grid? _____

5. What highway passes by the San Francisco Airport? _____

6. What island is a park? _____

7. How many miles is it from San Leandro to San Rafael? _____

B. On separate paper, describe how you would travel from Pacifica to Lafayette.

Sequence

The order in which things happen in a story is called **sequence.** Some things may happen at different times, and some things may happen at the same time.

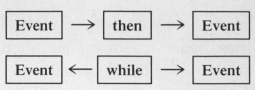

Read each story. Write a sentence to answer each question.

As Mark poured orange juice into a glass, he spilled some of it. He wiped up the spill, then he drank the juice.

1. What did Mark do at the same time that he poured orange juice?

_____

2. What was the last thing Mark did?

_____

After Ben painted a picture of a dragon, he left it to dry. He framed his picture and hung it on the wall.

3. What was the second thing Ben did?

_____

4. What did Ben do before he put his picture up?

_____

Rosa decided to build a bird feeder. She found some scraps of wood. While she was building the feeder, her mother helped her. After the bird feeder was all finished, Rosa filled it with birdseed. Then she put the feeder outside for the birds.

5. What was the first thing Rosa did after deciding to make a bird feeder?

_____

6. What did Rosa's mother do while Rosa was building the feeder?

_____

7. What was the last thing Rosa did before she put the bird feeder outside?

_____

Inference

Authors do not always explain every detail in a story. Readers must figure out some things on their own. You can use information given in the story and your own experience to understand something that is not directly stated in the story. When you do this, you are making an **inference.**

┌──────────────────┐
│   Story Clues   │
└──────────────────┘
┌──────────────────┐
+ │ Experience Clues │
└──────────────────┘
┌──────────────────┐
│   Inference   │
└──────────────────┘

   Example: Some people long ago wrote messages from right to left.
        Inference: We write in the opposite direction from some people of long ago.

Can you tell why this inference statement is true? It is true because the sentence tells us that many people of long ago wrote from right to left, and we know that we write messages from left to right.

Read about the ancient system of picture writing. Then read the inference statements. Complete the sentence that tells why each inference statement is true.

   Some people of long ago wrote with pictures, not with letters. Several pictures together made up a message. These picture messages were carved on walls. Picture writing was used from 3,000 B.C. until about A.D. 400. Many examples of picture writing are still preserved and studied today.

1. **Inference:** We would not be able to read a picture message very easily. We know that this is true because the paragraph says that

   _____

   _____

2. **Inference:** Picture writing was an important system for a very long time. We know that this is true because the paragraph says that

   _____

   _____

3. **Inference:** Modern people try to save some of the picture writing from long ago. We know that this is true because the paragraph says that

   _____

   _____

Long Word Decoding

When you read long words, use what you know about word parts and about syllables to figure out how to pronounce the word. Follow these rules:

1. Look for words or word parts you know. (*doorway*, happi*ness*, *re*turn)

2. Divide what is left into syllables. (hap pi ness)

3. Say each part slowly.

4. Try out different vowel sounds. (cap, case, car)

Here are some long words. Finish each sentence by circling the correct answer.

deactivate   (to make something become not active)

1. The prefix in the first syllable is _____ .   de   dis   ac

2. The *e* in the first syllable sounds like the *e* in _____ .   me   her   them

3. The *a* in the second syllable sounds like the *a* in _____ .   ate   ask   car

4. The *a* in the fourth syllable sounds like the *a* in _____ .   jaw   hat   take

5. There are _____ syllables in *deactivate*.   3   4   5

punctual   (doing something right on time)

6. The first two syllables look like those in _____ .   punish   punctuate   punchy

7. The *al* in this word sounds like the *al* in _____ .   sale   fall   journal

8. There are _____ syllables in *punctual*.   3   4   5

bandleader   (a person who leads a band)

9. The *a* in the first syllable sounds like the *a* in _____ .   late   cape   ham

10. In the third syllable, *ea* sounds like the sound in _____ .   be   ten   ready

11. There are _____ syllables in *bandleader*.   3   4   5

12. The suffix in this word is _____ .   or   ade   er

13. *Bandleader* is a compound word. Write the two words that form *bandleader*.

_____   _____

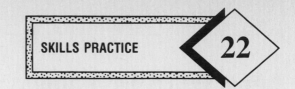

Main Idea/Details

The **main idea** tells what a paragraph is about. All the **details** should support, or tell about, the main idea. When the main idea is stated, there is one sentence in the paragraph that tells the main idea. When the main idea is not stated, there is no main idea sentence. You must decide on the main idea by thinking of a sentence that tells about all the details.

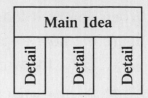

A. Read each paragraph. Underline the sentence that states the main idea. Then read the sentences below each paragraph. Circle one or two that could support the main idea. Draw a line through the sentence or sentences that would *not* support the main idea.

1. The leaves on a tree make food. The inner bark of the tree carries the food. The outer bark protects the tree. Each part of a tree has a special job.

Some trees grow very tall.

The roots hold the tree in place.

Maple leaves change color in fall.

2. Long ago, people considered a small amount of pepper a treasure. Kings were glad to get such a gift. Taxes were paid with pepper in some countries. Historical records tell of ransoms being paid with this seasoning, too. Pepper was much more valuable in the past than it is now.

Pepper was valuable because it made meat that was almost spoiling taste all right.

Poor people rarely had any pepper.

Pepper is a finely ground seasoning.

B. Read the paragraph. Circle the sentence that tells the main idea.

3. To make a bookworm, tack a paper bookworm head to a bulletin board. Then cut 5-inch paper worm segments. Each time a classmate reads a book, write the title and the reader's name on a segment. Add the segments to the bookworm.

It is fun to read interesting books.

It is fun and easy to make a class bookworm.

All you need is paper, scissors, and imagination.

Vocabulary: Story Critical Words

A. Study the meaning of each word.

advice   a suggestion about what to do or how to do it

daring   fearless; bold

expert   having special knowledge and experience

rewarding   giving a good feeling

selection   a thing chosen

serious   not joking or foolish; sincere

B. Read the paragraph. Finish each incomplete sentence with the correct vocabulary word.

   Juan wanted to climb the highest mountain in the region. Even though he was very experienced, he asked his friend Terri for _____. She was a mountain ranger and an _____ on the region. Terri told Juan that he was quite _____ to attempt the climb. Juan said he was _____ about the challenge and asked Terri what things he should take along. She helped him make the right _____ of equipment. Terri told Juan that even if he didn't reach the mountain peak the first time, he would still find the experience _____ .

C. Each word below is a synonym or an antonym for a vocabulary word. Write the vocabulary word. Then write **S** if it is a synonym or **A** if it is an antonym.

1. funny _____

2. pleasing _____

3. specialist _____

4. fearful _____

D. Write the vocabulary word each sentence tells about.

5. People who give this are trying to be helpful. _____

6. Someone who knows a lot about something is this. _____

7. Doing a kind act for someone else can be this for you. _____

8. You might call a person who is not afraid to go on a roller coaster this. _____

© Silver, Burdett & Ginn Inc.

Vocabulary: Support Words

A. Study the meaning of each word.

breakthrough   an important discovery
chisel   a sharp tool used to cut or shape stone or wood
citizen   a member of a country or state
illustrating   drawing pictures to explain or decorate

inspiration   something that stirs action or thought
revisiting   visiting again
sculpture   the art of making statues
session   a meeting

B. Answer each question with the correct vocabulary word.

1. What must you be to vote? _____

2. What might create a breakthrough? _____

3. What is new and exciting? _____

4. What does a woodcarver use? _____

5. What is a statue? _____

6. Which word has a prefix that means "again?" _____

7. What might an artist be doing for a storybook? _____

8. What might a band organize in order to practice? _____

C. Complete each analogy by writing the correct vocabulary word.

9. *Needle* is to *sewing box* as _____ is to *toolbox*.

10. *Looking* is to *watching* as _____ is to *showing*.

11. *Cup* is to *mug* as _____ is to *discovery*.

D. Complete the paragraph by writing the correct vocabulary words.

Amy and Ken were _____ the art museum. Amy really liked

the _____ she saw. It was made of wood and had been carved

with a _____. Ken wondered what the sculptor's

_____ had been for making it.

Suffixes *-en, -ous*

A **suffix** is a word part added to the end of a word. It changes the meaning of the word and the way the word is used in a sentence.

-ous, -ious: "having the qualities of" forms an adjective

-en: "made of" forms an adjective "cause to be" forms a verb

Follow these rules when adding a suffix beginning with a vowel letter.

If a final *y* follows a consonant, drop the *y*. (fury + *-ious* = furious)

If a one-syllable word ends with a single consonant letter preceded by a vowel letter, usually double the consonant letter. (flat + *-en* = flatten)

The final *e* is usually dropped. (shake + *-en* = shaken; adventure + *-ous* = adventurous)

Complete each sentence by adding *-en, -ious,* or *-ous* to the underlined word in parentheses. Use the meaning clues to choose the correct suffix.

1. Since the play, Marie has become quite _____ .
   (having the qualities of <u>fame</u>)

2. Her costume looked like shiny, _____ metal.
   (made of <u>gold</u>)

3. Marie sang the songs in a _____ voice.
   (having the qualities of <u>glory</u>)

4. The play ended in a _____ way.
   (having the qualities of <u>joy</u>)

5. A snowflake is a _____ thing.
   (having the qualities of <u>mystery</u>)

6. The _____ pottery was broken.
   (made of <u>earth</u>)

7. He was _____ when he lost the game.
   (having the qualities of <u>fury</u>)

8. He had an _____ look.
   (made of <u>ashes</u>)

Main Idea/Details

The **main idea** tells what the paragraph is about. All the **details** in the paragraph should support the main idea. When the main idea is unstated, you can decide what the main idea is by thinking of a sentence that tells about all the details.

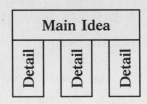

A. Write the details that support each main idea. Then draw a line through the nonsupporting detail, the sentence that does *not* support the main idea. **MI** stands for main idea. **SD** stands for supporting details.

1. MI   Many stories are about magical animals.

   SD   _____

   SD   _____
   Some stories tell about flying horses.
   Animals are exciting to read about.
   Dragons are described in many tales.

2. MI   A modern kitchen has many helpful machines.

   SD   _____

   SD   _____

   SD   _____
   The kitchen is a popular room.
   The refrigerator keeps the food cold.
   The stove is used to cook the food.
   The dishwasher cleans the dishes.

B. Read the detail sentences. Decide what the main idea is and write it.

3. Often, an actor must practice for many hours. Many pages of lines must be learned for each role. Over time, an actor may play many different characters. These roles may demand that the actor demonstrate different emotions and character traits. An actor may even be required to play characters that are much older or younger than he or she really is.

   Main Idea: _____

   _____

Multiple Meanings

A **multiple meaning** word is a word with more than one meaning. Read the example.

Example: Kim likes to <u>play</u> chess. (''take part in a game'')
Our class put on a <u>play</u>. (''a story that is acted out'')

Some riddles are based on two different meanings of one word. For each word, read the meanings and the riddle. Write the two meanings that make the riddle funny.

sock

1. a short, knitted covering for the foot
2. a hard blow
3. to hit hard, especially with the fist
4. to set money away as savings

Why did Sal's foot jump backwards?
It was going to get a <u>sock</u>!

_____

_____

pool

1. a game played with hard balls on a special table
2. an amount of money shared by a group
3. a puddle or pond
4. to put together for the use of all

Why was the table under water?
It was used for playing <u>pool</u>!

_____

_____

patch

1. a small bit or piece of material
2. a small piece of ground
3. to put a patch on something to mend it
4. to make in a hurry

Why did Bill Bunny put a little piece of cloth on the ground?
He wanted his own garden <u>patch</u>!

_____

_____

ring

1. a line or edge forming a circle
2. a band worn on the finger
3. to make a circle around
4. to make the sound of a bell

Why did the groom put the wedding band to his ear?
He wanted to hear it <u>ring</u>!

_____

_____

Charts

A. The chart shows how four fourth-graders, Bob, Lena, Miguel, and Rudi, kept track of the number and types of books they read on their own during the past few weeks. Study their chart. Then answer the questions.

	Adventure	Biographies	Poetry	Mysteries
Bob	2	3	0	2
Lena	1	2	3	1
Miguel	2	1	2	2
Rudi	3	3	1	2

1. Which type of book on the chart was the most popular? _____

   How did you decide? _____

2. Which type of book did the children read the least? _____

3. Who read the most books? _____

4. Who read more books of poems, Miguel or Lena? _____

5. Which two children each read three biographies? _____

6. Which children read the same number of mystery books?

   _____

B. Make a chart for you and three friends. List these types of books: animal stories, folktales, historical fiction, science fiction.

Fantasy

Fantasy is a kind of fiction that tells about people, things, and events that could not really happen. Fantasies come from the author's imagination. Reading fantasies can expand your own imagination.

> In a story, what could happen only in an imaginary world is *fantasy*. What could happen in real life is *realistic*.

A. Read the story. Then write the word **fantasy** or **realistic** next to each sentence in the list.

Racing Deer arrived at the park when it was nearly empty. Only a few small children played on a giant slide while their parents watched. Racing Deer jumped onto the third swing. She felt as if she were flying! The tops of the trees seemed so close. The houses looked small.

Suddenly a huge bird landed on a tree. The bird said, ''Will you help me, little one?''

Racing Deer kept swinging. ''How can I help you?'' she asked.

''Once I was a strong eagle. Now I am just a poor crow,'' said the bird. ''I lived at Pink Rock. I made the sun rise and set.'' The crow gave her a large black feather. ''Wear this feather and you can fly with me to Pink Rock.''

Racing Deer took the feather. Her arms became long, dark wings.

1. Racing Deer jumped onto the third swing. _____

2. The bird said, ''Will you help me, little one?'' _____

3. Racing Deer kept swinging. _____

4. The crow gave her a large black feather. _____

5. Her arms became long, dark wings. _____

B. On separate paper, write a fantasy sentence to add to the story about Racing Deer.

Vocabulary: Story Critical Words

A. Study the meaning of each word.

apologize to say that one is sorry	**infectious** tending to spread to others
awkward uncomfortable; difficult	**offended** insulted
contentedly happily	**tragedy** a sad happening
evidently easily seen or understood	**undignified** without dignity; improper

B. Read about each situation. Write the vocabulary word that can be used in the situation.

1. If you arrive at a party before everything is ready, you might feel this way.

_____

2. If you accidentally stepped on someone's foot, you would do this.

_____

3. If you interrupt people who are talking, they might feel this way.

_____

4. A doctor will tell you to stay home if he thinks your illness is this.

_____

5. If a natural disaster destroys many homes, it will be called this.

_____

6. If you stroke a cat, it might purr this way.   _____

7. Something that is plain to see stands out this way.   _____

8. Someone who goes into a restaurant without shoes might appear this way.

_____

C. Finish each sentence with the correct vocabulary word.

9. Mr. Banks had to _____ to the doctor because he was late for his appointment.

10. Ken read about a _____ in which a flood destroyed a town.

11. Some diseases can be _____ .

12. It feels _____ to fall flat on one's face.

Vocabulary: Support Words

A. Study the meaning of each word.

distressing upsetting
floundering struggling in a clumsy way
flung thrown with force
gracious polite and charming

heartily sincerely; with enthusiasm
lurching moving jerkily, in a stop-start way
murmuring speaking in a low voice
outraged very angry

B. Finish each sentence with the correct vocabulary word. Write the word in the puzzle.

Across

  4. Ted _____ the ball.

  5. The trapped fish was _____.

  7. Nan welcomed her friend _____.

  8. Ralph is a _____ host.

Down

  1. The wrongly accused man felt _____.

  2. The teammates were _____ so their opponents couldn't hear.

  3. She found the sad news _____.

  6. The car was _____ along the rough road.

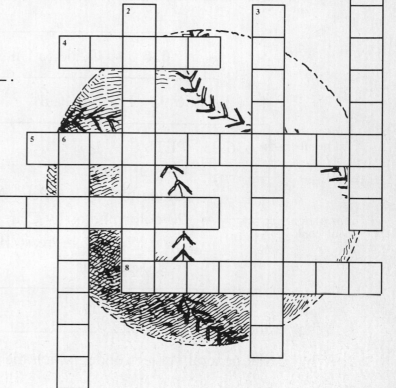

C. Write the vocabulary word each sentence tells about.

  9. You might laugh this way at a funny joke. _____

  10. You might be speaking this way if you were telling a friend a secret.

    _____

  11. You might feel this way if someone borrowed something from you without asking first. _____

Card Catalog

All the fiction and nonfiction books in the library are listed on cards or on a computer listing. Cards are in alphabetical order in separate drawers of the **card catalog.** There are three kinds of cards or listings for each nonfiction book—a **title card,** an **author card,** and a **subject card.** You can find these cards in the following ways:

title card: when you know the title of a book
author card: when you know the author's name
subject card: when there is a particular subject you want to read about

Study the cards. Use the information on the cards to answer each question.

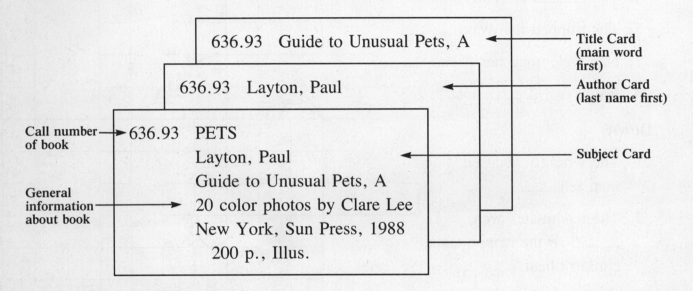

1. What is the title of the book? _____

2. What is the general subject under which the book is listed? _____

3. Who is the author of the book? _____

4. What company published the book? _____

5. When and where was the book published? _____

6. How long is the book? _____

7. Is this book illustrated? _____

8. What is its call number? _____

9. How many and what kind of illustrations does it have? _____

10. Who is the photographer? _____

Suffixes *-en, -ous*

A **suffix** is a word part added to the end of a word. It changes the meaning of the word and the way the word is used in a sentence. Read the meanings of the suffixes *-en* and *-ous*.

> *-ous, -ious:* "having the qualities of"—forms an adjective *(dangerous, furious)*
> *-en:* "made of"—forms an adjective *(woolen)*
> "cause to be"—forms a verb *(sharpen, flatten)*

Complete the sentences by adding *-en*, *-ious*, or *-ous* to the underlined word. Use context clues in the sentences and the meanings of the prefixes to help you. Write the new word.

1. Trong liked <u>adventure</u>. He was _____ .

2. Ted knew they might face <u>danger</u> on this trip.

   He knew the trip might be _____ .

3. These two explorers usually had <u>nerves</u> of steel.

   But now they felt a bit _____ .

4. Ted wanted to keep his senses <u>sharp</u>.

   He tried to _____ his senses by staying alert.

5. They found a wheel made of <u>wood</u>.

   They knew that this _____ wheel was very old.

6. Trong picked up a box filled with cloth made of <u>silk</u>.

   The _____ cloth was still soft.

7. They wondered who <u>hid</u> these treasures.

   The _____ treasures puzzled them.

8. Why these things were left here was a <u>mystery</u>.

   It was a _____ question!

Sequence

The order in which things happen in a story is called the **sequence.** Time order clue words can help you determine the correct sequence. As you read, look for words like *next, after, then, first, second, later,* and *until.* Sometimes two events happen at the same time. Look for words like *while, as,* and *during.*

Example: As Dan put on his coat the phone rang. He answered the call. Then he wrote a message.

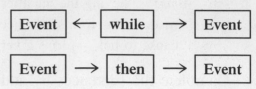

A. Read each sentence. Answer each question by writing a sentence.

1. Sam shut off the alarm. Then he got out of bed.

   What happened first? _____

   What happened second? _____

2. As Sam ate breakfast he read the newspaper. Later he called Jill.

   What happened at the same time? _____

   _____

3. Jill answered the phone. She and Sam planned a ball game while they talked.

   What happened at the same time? _____

   _____

4. Sam packed his lunch, made his bed, and left the house.

   What happened last? _____

5. After they met at the corner, Sam and Jill walked together.

   What happened first? _____

6. While they walked to the park, they talked. Later they met their friends.

   What happened at the same time? _____

   What happened after that? _____

B. On separate paper, list the time order clue words used in the sentences. Write sentences using each one. Make diagrams like the ones in the example for each one.

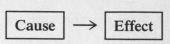
Cause/Effect

When one event makes another event happen, there is a **cause** and an **effect.** Sometimes words like *because, since, so,* and *therefore* signal a cause and effect. Read the example. Each cause is underlined and each effect is circled. Notice that in the first example, there is no signal word.

Cause → Effect

Examples: <u>Last week Lily broke her ankle.</u> She has to wear a cast.

<u>Since she uses crutches,</u> her friends carry her books.

A. Read the paragraph. Match the cause and effect statements. Write the letter of the effect next to the cause it matches.

My Aunt Jo loves to write plays. I asked her if she would write a play for my class. Since she had some spare time, she agreed to do it. The play was very funny; therefore, it was a big hit with everyone. We wanted to show our thanks. At the opening performance, the class gave Aunt Jo a bouquet of flowers.

Cause

1. ____ The play was very funny.

2. ____ Aunt Jo loves to write plays.

3. ____ We wanted to show our thanks.

4. ____ She had some spare time.

Effect

a. The class gave flowers to Aunt Jo.

b. The play was a big hit.

c. She agreed to write the play.

d. I asked my aunt to write a play for my class.

B. In the paragraph, underline the causes. Circle the effects.

Cal's friend Randy had moved away, so Cal decided to write him a letter. Randy had been gone for nearly a month. Cal had many things to tell him. Because he didn't want to forget anything, he jotted some notes first. Cal had a very good memory. The letter he wrote was almost four pages long! Since Cal wanted the letter to get out that day, he walked to the post office instead of the nearest mailbox.

C. Write one more cause and effect that could fit in the paragraph.

_____

_____

Main Idea/Details

A **topic** is the subject of a piece of writing. The **main idea** (MI) tells what a whole paragraph is about. The **supporting details** (SD) tell more about the main idea. In some paragraphs, the main idea is not stated. Then you must figure out the main idea from the details.

Main Idea		
Detail	Detail	Detail

Example: **(SD)** Dinosaurs and woolly mammoths are animals that are no longer around. **(SD)** Saber-toothed tigers have also been gone for a long time. **(MI)** These animals no longer live on the earth.

Topic: Extinct Animals

Read each paragraph. Choose the main idea. Draw a circle around it. Then write a word that tells what the topic is.

1. The Pilgrims faced freezing winter weather. In spring, they did not know what seeds to plant in the rocky soil. They also did not know how to prepare the soil.

   The Pilgrims did not like the cold weather.   Topic: _____

   The Pilgrims were not prepared for what they had to face.

   The Pilgrims did not like rocky soil.

2. In volleyball, players hit a large ball back and forth over a net. Badminton players hit an object called a birdie back and forth over a net. In tennis, players hit a small ball back and forth over a net.

   Some sports involve hitting an object over a net.   Topic: _____

   In some sports there are two or more players.

   Volleyball is a great sport.

3. Cats are loving and playful. They never need to be walked. They are happy indoors or outdoors. They carefully clean themselves every day.

   Cats and dogs can be trained.   Topic: _____

   Cats like to be indoors.

   Cats make great pets.

Vocabulary: Story Critical Words

A. Study the meaning of each word.

combination two or more things joined
developed treated photographic film with chemicals to make a picture appear
effects impressions made on the mind; results
film material used for taking photographs

invented created
projection an image shown on a surface, such as a screen
projects causes an image to be seen on a surface
rewound coiled again

B. Complete each sentence with a vocabulary word.

1. Tim put a new roll of _____ into his camera.

2. Julia and Carla saw a movie that was a _____ of thriller and science fiction.

3. The theater owner _____ the movie onto the screen.

4. Special _____ in the movie created the impression of traveling through outer space.

5. The movie maker _____ some interesting robotlike characters.

6. At the end of the movie, someone _____ the film to prepare for the next screening.

C. Answer each question with the correct vocabulary word.

7. What do you need to put in a camera to take pictures? _____

8. After you took your pictures, what was done to the film to make them appear?

   _____

9. What do you see on a screen when you look at a movie? _____

D. Read each word. Draw a ✔ mark on the line if the word is spelled correctly. If the word is spelled incorrectly, rewrite the word correctly.

10. invented _____

11. developed _____

12. projecs _____

13. film _____

Vocabulary: Support Words

A. Study the meaning of each word.

animated   made a movie by filming a series of drawings

background   the back part of a scene

imagination   the power to make up pictures or ideas in the mind

miniature   a very small copy or model

realistic   true to life; real-looking

scene   view; landscape

techniques   ways of using tools and materials

B. Find and circle six vocabulary words hidden in the puzzle. The words go across and down. Write each word. The first one has been done for you.

b	l	u	i	t	s	c	a	l	t	e	b
a	n	i	m	a	t	e	d	s	a	r	e
c	o	o	a	r	h	s	e	s	t	l	c
k	e	l	g	e	o	r	n	p	o	t	k
g	o	m	i	n	i	a	t	u	r	e	g
r	i	s	n	f	s	e	f	d	o	c	o
o	s	t	a	d	r	b	c	u	e	h	u
u	t	e	t	e	e	r	d	n	g	n	n
n	e	d	i	a	d	e	s	r	r	i	d
d	d	r	o	b	m	a	t	d	e	q	c
c	e	n	n	d	s	t	a	e	r	u	e
s	c	e	n	e	t	e	t	n	b	e	n
n	i	a	t	u	e	a	n	b	i	s	e

1. background _____
2. _____
3. _____
4. _____
5. _____
6. _____

C. Answer each question with a vocabulary word.

7. What is an antonym for *phony*? _____

8. What is a synonym for *foreground*? _____

D. Complete each sentence with the correct vocabulary word.

9. ''Sleeping Beauty'' is an _____ movie.

10. Mark has a good _____ when it comes to drawing pictures.

Index

Many nonfiction books have an **index** located at the back of the book. The index lists all the topics covered in the book. These topics are listed alphabetically. Page numbers beside each topic tell where the topic can be found in the book. The *m* next to the page number indicates a map on the topic. Read the example.

Example: Food
               in early settlements, 73–76
               storage of, 74, 76

This portion of an index says that information on the topic of food in early settlements can be found on pages 73, 74, 75, and 76. It also says that information on the topic of the storage of food can be found on two pages, 74 and 76.

Look at the following section of an index. Use the information in the index to answer the questions.

INDEX

Farming, 54–62
    changes in area of, 53
    dry, 53
    in early settlements, 54–56
    tree, 57–58
Farm products, 60*m*

Federal government, 65–67

Feed crops, 56

Ferguson, Mary, 102

Fire departments, 142, 150

Fishing, 70–82
    by early Native Americans, 71–73
    by settlers, 73–75
    in oceans, 77*m*
    in rivers, 76
    products of, 76, 79–81

1. On what pages could you find information about farming in early American settlements? _____

2. How many pages give information about tree farming? _____

3. Does this book contain information about changes in the area of farming? _____

4. What pages describe fire departments? _____

5. What two maps are listed in this index with the letter *m?*

_____

6. Where can information on fishing by early Native Americans be found?

_____

Card Catalog

In the library, books are listed alphabetically by author, title, or subject in a **card catalog** or a computer listing. For each nonfiction book there is a **title card,** an **author card,** and a **subject card.** A call number usually appears at the top of each card. Remember to use these cards in the following ways:

title card: when you know the title of a book
author card: when you know the author's name
subject card: when there is a particular subject you want to read about

A. Study the cards. Then write the type of card each one is.

794.82	Best in Video Games, The
	Dale, Janet
	Chicago, New Press, 1988
	250 p., Illus.

794.82	Dale, Janet
	Best in Video Games, The
	Chicago, New Press, 1988
	250 p., Illus.

1. _____

2. _____

B. Use the information on the cards to complete the following sentences.

3. The title of the book is _____.

4. The author's name is _____.

5. The total number of pages in the book is _____.

6. The call number of the book is _____.

C. Write the word or words you would look under in the card catalog to find the following items.

7. another book by Janet Dale _____

8. the author of *Computer Action* _____

9. a book about the history of electronics _____

10. a book written by Juan Martinez _____

11. a book about special effects in the movies _____

12. a book about famous movies _____

Main Idea/Details

In a paragraph, the **main idea** tells what the whole paragraph is about. **Details** support, or tell about, the main idea. Sometimes the main idea is stated. When the main idea is *not* stated directly, you must figure it out from the details.

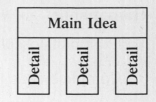

A. Read each paragraph. Choose the main idea, and then write it.

1. A young goose is called a gosling. Kids are young goats. A young deer is a fawn. Young coyotes and wolves are called pups.

Main Idea: _____

_____

Young animals have many lessons to learn.
Some young animals are called different names than their parents.
Young dogs and young whales are also called pups.

2. First, cut off the top of a large milk carton. Punch two or three small holes in the bottom for drainage. Fill three fourths of the carton with soil. Plant tomato seeds about one-half inch under the soil. Then water the soil. Place the carton in a warm, sunny place. Water the seeds now and then to keep the soil moist. Finally, watch your tomato plant sprout and grow.

Main Idea: _____

_____

Some plants have to be grown in gardens.
Tomato plants like moist soil and sunlight.
The steps to follow for growing a tomato plant are easy.

B. Read the paragraph. Underline the main idea. Then read the details. Cross out the detail that would not support the main idea.

3. Mountain goats live in high, rocky mountains. Lions and zebras live in grasslands. The marsh is home to snakes and alligators. Animals live in many kinds of places.

Grassland animals eat grasses and leaves.   The roadrunner's home is in the desert.

Homophones

Homophones are words that sound the same but have different spellings and meanings.

Example: Joseph <u>ate</u> one banana and <u>eight</u> grapes.

Complete each pair of sentences by writing the correct homophone.

1. sea—see

Millie was walking toward the beach by the _____ .

She could _____ the waves breaking on the shore.

2. blew—blue

The sky was clear and bright _____ .

The wind _____ in strong gusts.

3. hear—here

From a nearby boat, Millie could _____ a voice calling.

A man in the boat yelled, "Come _____ and help!"

4. plane—plain

The look of fear was _____ on the man's face.

He told Millie that a small _____ was damaged and slowly submerging a few miles out. He said he had to maintain radio contact with them.

5. right—write

"I'll go to the telephone booth near the main dock and call for help _____ away," said Millie.

The man said, "I'll _____ down the number of Sea Rescue for you."

6. weight—wait

Luckily, they didn't have to _____ long for the rescue team to arrive.

After the rescue, Millie felt as if a _____ had been lifted from her shoulders.

7. know—no

"I _____ I'll never see anything like that again," Millie said.

"_____ , you probably won't," said the man.

Inference

Authors do not always explain every detail in a story. Often readers must figure out some things on their own. When you use information given in the story and your own experience to understand something that is not stated directly, you are **making an inference.**

Story Clues
Experience Clues
Inference

+

Read the story. Write answers to the questions.

Roy was spending his first night at his Uncle Ted's farmhouse in the country. Roy climbed into bed and tried to go to sleep. But he was not used to all the quiet. He kept listening for the familiar background sounds of voices chatting and horns honking. Just as he was finally about to fall asleep, he heard a noise. Something was scratching and brushing against the bedroom door. Roy froze. Who or what could it be? He listened. Then, after what seemed like forever, the noise stopped.

Early the next morning, he joined his uncle at breakfast. Still sleepy-eyed, Roy met the farm cat, Marigold. Uncle Ted explained that Marigold was a "watch cat." She often roamed about the house at night, making sure everything was OK. Seeing the look of relief on Roy's face, Uncle Ted added that tonight he would let Marigold stay outside.

1. Where did Roy live? _____

2. What clues helped you to answer question 1? _____

_____

_____

3. What was the noise that Roy heard? _____

_____

4. Why did Roy freeze when he heard the noise? _____

_____

5. Why would Uncle Ted let Marigold stay outside that night? _____

_____

_____

Vocabulary: Story Critical Words

A. Study the meaning of each word.

emotion a strong feeling
entertained amused
evidence proof
newsstand a stand where newspapers and
magazines are sold

punishment what is done to people to make
them pay for wrongdoing
register a machine for counting and keeping
records
resolved made up one's mind

B. Complete each analogy with the correct vocabulary word.

1. *Apple* is to *fruit* as *love* is to _____ .

2. *Gas* is to *gas station* as *magazine* is to _____ .

3. *Good* is to *bad* as *reward* is to _____ .

4. *Fixed* is to *repaired* as *decided* is to _____ .

C. Answer each question.

5. Which vocabulary word is made up of two smaller words? Write the word and

draw a line (/) between the two words. _____

6. When you shop, where do you go to pay? to the _____

7. What can prove if a person is innocent or guilty of a crime?

_____

8. What is given to a person who commits a crime? _____

9. What did the magician do at the party? He _____ .

10. What is sadness? an _____

D. Finish each sentence with the correct vocabulary word.

11. Maureen bought a magazine at the _____ .

12. Fear is not a pleasant _____ to feel.

13. Mom went to the cash _____ to pay for the groceries.

14. As _____ for not cleaning her room, Alice could not watch TV.

Vocabulary: Support Words

A. Study the meaning of each word.

accuse   to blame
avenue   a wide street
bail   money given to guarantee that an accused person will appear for trial
conductor   a person who collects fares on
 buses and trains

disbelief   a lack of belief
honorable   honest and sincere
nervously   restlessly; fearfully
skinflint   a stingy person

B. Complete each riddle with the correct vocabulary word.

1. I am a person who doesn't like to spend money. I am a _____ .

2. Traffic is always moving over me. I am an _____ .

3. You may have heard me say, "Tickets, please." I am a _____ .

C. Finish each sentence with the correct vocabulary word.

4. I paid my busfare to the _____ .

5. You can always trust an _____ person.

6. The police will _____ the man of robbing the bank.

7. Mary cried out in _____ when she won the contest.

8. Jack is such a _____ , unlike his generous brother.

D. There are five misspelled words in the following paragraph. Read the paragraph.
Circle each misspelled word. Write the correct spelling for each word.

The jester sat nervusly in the courtroom.

"I acuse you of making fun of our honerable mayor," said the lawyer.

The jester said in disbelieve. "But I thought it was my job to make people laugh."

The judge nodded. "I will have to think this over for a day," he said. "Mean-
while, bale for the jester is set at two oranges and one peanut."

9. _____   12. _____

10. _____   13. _____

11. _____

Summarizing

A **summary** is a short statement in your own words that gives the main points of what you have read. A summary tells only the most important information, while telling a whole story.

Read the story about Walt's dream. Then write a three-sentence summary of the story.

Walt had just come home from seeing the movie *King Arthur's Grand Adventure*. The movie had really impressed him. He went over the movie in his mind as he ate an apple and a piece of cheese.

After his snack, Walt felt sleepy. He flopped down on his bed. His head had barely hit the pillow when he fell into a deep sleep and started to dream.

Walt dreamed that he was a knight on horseback, riding through an open field. In the distance he saw a shimmering castle that reached to the clouds. Then he came upon a group of field workers who called out to him.

"Good day, my lord," they said.

"What?" he replied in a half sleep. At that moment, Walt woke up. He realized that his dream was like the movie — and he was King Arthur himself!

Sentence 1: _____

_____

Sentence 2: _____

_____

Sentence 3: _____

_____

Does your summary tell only the most important things, yet still tell a whole story?

© Silver, Burdett & Ginn Inc.

Suffixes *-en, -ous*

A **suffix** is a word part added to the end of a word. It changes the meaning of the word and the way the word is used in a sentence. Read the meanings of the suffixes *-ous*, *-ious*, and *-en*.

> *-ous, -ious:* "having the qualities of," forms an adjective   *famous, glorious*
> *-en:* "made of," forms an adjective   *silken*
>   "cause to be," forms a verb   *whiten*

A. Read the sentences. Write a definition for each underlined word.

1. The material was soft and <u>silken</u> to the touch. (adjective)

   _____

2. The cement will <u>harden</u> quickly. (verb) _____

3. The cat's <u>mysterious</u> disappearance was not noticed. (adjective)

   _____

4. Most people need to <u>sharpen</u> their writing skills. (verb) _____

5. Never be <u>envious</u> of someone's good fortune! (adjective) _____

   _____

B. Read the words and their clues. Write three sentences using one of the words in each sentence.

ambitious (adjective)	strengthen (verb)	wondrous (adjective)

6. _____

   _____

7. _____

   _____

8. _____

   _____

Card Catalog

In the library, fiction and nonfiction books are listed on cards in a card catalog or on a computer listing. All the cards are arranged in alphabetical order. For each nonfiction book, there are three types of cards—a **title card,** an **author card,** and a **subject card.**

A. These three cards are from a card catalog. Write the type of card each one is.

398.29 Carr, Lawrence, Jr. Folktales of America

398.29 Folktales, American Carr, Lawrence, Jr. Folktales of America

1. _____

2. _____

398.29 Folktales of America Carr, Lawrence, Jr.

3. _____

B. Write the type of card you would look for in the card catalog if you wanted to find more information on each item.

4. a book entitled *Max, My Hearing-Ear Dog* _____

5. the illustrations in *Those Amazing Chimpanzees!* _____

6. a book Susan Marx wrote about a basketball superstar _____

7. Mexican folklore _____

8. books by Louisa May Alcott _____

9. the call number for *Safe Backpacking for Beginners* _____

10. a book about Martin Luther King, Jr. _____

11. a book entitled *The Swimming Lesson* _____

12. contact lenses _____

13. Mardi Gras _____

14. a book by Jamie Thompson _____

Figurative Language

Writers use figurative language to describe things in an imaginative way. Read the examples of figurative language.

Examples: My new <u>mittens</u> feel <u>as soft as a baby rabbit</u>. (simile)

That yellow <u>balloon is a spot of sunshine</u>. (metaphor)

The mayor decided to <u>come clean</u> and admit the mistake. (idiom)

Read the paragraph. Then follow the directions.

The quiet, empty town was a silent desert. Rory saw a storm cloud that looked like a dark curtain. The wind howled and whined like a wild wolf. Suddenly, the flying grains of sand were tiny needles against his face. Rory kept his cool. He quickly covered his eyes and raced for home. Rory was so tired that he hit the hay early.

A. Write the sentences that compare two different things using *like* or *as*.

1. _____

_____

2. _____

B. Write the sentences that compare two different things using *is, are, was,* or *were*.

3. _____

4. _____

_____

C. Write the meaning of each idiom. To interpret an idiom, try and "see" its specific action in your mind. Then make its meaning more general.

5. kept his cool

_____

6. hit the spot

_____

7. get out of line

_____

8. go all out

_____

9. strike out

_____

10. in the bag

_____

Classification

Words can be classified, or grouped together, according to ways in which they are alike. The whole group of words is called a category or a class.

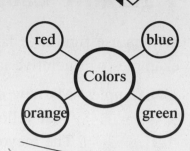

red   blue   Colors   orange   green

A. Read each numbered row of words. Put an **X** on the word that does not belong. Then write a new word from the box that fits each classification.

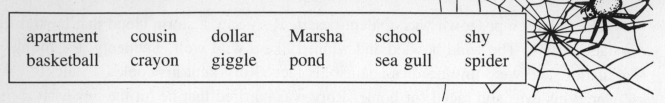

| apartment | cousin | dollar | Marsha | school | shy |
| basketball | crayon | giggle | pond | sea gull | spider |

1. pencil   chalk   pen   purple   paintbrush   _____

2. disappointed   contest   happy   afraid   brave   _____

3. doctor   factory   library   hospital   store   _____

4. dime   nickel   pocket   quarter   penny   _____

5. ladybug   nest   moth   cricket   caterpillar   _____

6. soccer   hockey   volleyball   tennis   gym   _____

7. laugh   smile   chuckle   clap   grin   _____

8. Maria   Molly   Madeline   Mindy   Michigan   _____

9. nephew   baby   aunt   sister   grandfather   _____

10. seashells   coral   seaweed   umbrellas   fish   _____

11. cabin   castle   road   cottage   farmhouse   _____

12. forest   stream   creek   river   waterfall   _____

B. On separate paper, write the name of each class of words to show how the words are related. For example, the words in row 11 might be called "Places to Live."

Inference

Sometimes writers do not tell you everything right in the story. When information is not stated directly, you can "read between the lines." Use clues in the story plus what you already know about things in the story to figure out the unstated information. This is called **making inferences.**

Story Clues
Experience Clues
Inference

+

Read the paragraph. Then answer the questions. Write the clues from the story and from your own experience that helped you make the inferences.

Diego cheered with the crowd. He could not take his eyes off Larry. That player's moves seemed impossible! Diego thought that Larry could move the ball, jump, and make the basket whenever he wanted to. During the game, he continued to study Larry's every move. Someday, he wanted to play just like him.

1. Where is Diego? _____

Story clues: _____

_____

Experience clues: _____

_____

2. Who is Larry? _____

Story clues: _____

_____

Experience clues: _____

_____

3. How does Diego feel about Larry? _____

_____

Story clues: _____

_____

Experience clues: _____

_____

Vocabulary: Story Critical Words

A. Study the meaning of each word.

perish   to die
prey   an animal hunted for food
riddles   puzzles in the form of questions
scarce   rare; uncommon

starvation   suffering from lack of food
troublesome   giving trouble
vigil   the act of watching or guarding
wolverine   an animal related to the weasel

B. Read each numbered item. The circled word in each item is incorrect. Write the vocabulary word that should go there.

1. Flowers will grow if they don't get enough water. _____

2. It's fun to figure out puddles. _____

3. The farmer found the broken plow helpful. _____

4. The furry goldfish chased a rat. _____

5. Several guards were posted around the castle in order to keep a laughing through the night. _____

6. The panther silently climbed up the tree to track its tail.

   _____

7. During a long period of dry weather, no grass grew.

   The cattle suffered from drowning. _____

8. Before the West was settled, great herds of buffalo roamed the plains.

   Now, however, buffalo are plentiful. _____

C. Finish each sentence with the correct vocabulary word.

9. Tracy likes to solve _____.

10. Owls like to hunt their _____ at night.

11. Water is _____ in the desert.

12. The nurse kept a _____ on her patient
    to make sure he would get well.

13. The librarian told the _____ student
    to stop making so much noise.

© Silver, Burdett & Ginn Inc.

Vocabulary: Support Words

A. Study the meaning of each word.

gait   a way of walking or running
gloomily   with deep sadness
halting   hesitating; unsure

paused   stopped for a short time
tundra   a large plain in the Arctic
wearily   in a tired manner

B. Finish each sentence with the correct vocabulary word. Write the word in the puzzle.

Across

   4. Snowstorms often sweep the
   _____ .

   6. The losing team returned _____ to
   the locker room.

Down

   1. The newborn foal had an awkward
   _____ .

   2. The speaker _____ and coughed.

   3. The tired traveler slumped _____
   into the seat.

   5. Because he could not remember his
   lines, the actor gave a _____
   performance.

C. Read each row of words. Draw an **X** through the word that does not rhyme. Then
write the vocabulary word that rhymes with the remaining words in the row.

   7. late   great   fit _____

   8. cheerily   surely   tearily _____

D. Write the vocabulary word that is a synonym for the underlined word.

   9. After a hard day at work, the man trudged <u>tiredly</u> up the stairs. _____

   10. Andrew looked <u>sadly</u> out of his window at the dreary weather outside.

   _____

Homographs

Words that are spelled the same but that have different pronunciations and different meanings are called **homographs.** *Bow* rhyming with *show* means "a knot tied with loops in it," and *bow* rhyming with *how* means "to bend the head or body." The words *bow* and *bow* are homographs.

Read the sentences. Write the meaning for each underlined homograph. Use the context clues to help you.

having life; not dead	papers showing permission	to make one's home
a kind of fish used for food	something being discussed	to force on someone
lowest kind of singing voice	to allow	

1. Kyle and Cindy looked forward to a day of fishing for <u>bass</u>.

_____

2. They heard a loud <u>bass</u> voice shout, "Hold on there!"

_____

3. A park ranger asked to see their fishing <u>permits</u>.

_____

4. He said, "I cannot <u>permit</u> you to fish here without that paper."

_____

5. "If you do fish, I must <u>subject</u> you to paying a fine."

_____

6. Cindy and Kyle quietly talked about the <u>subject</u> with the ranger.

_____

7. "I'm glad that we <u>live</u> near this beautiful park," said Kyle.

_____

8. "We can always come here to see different <u>live</u> animals," Cindy added.

_____

Classification

Classification helps you group words into a category or class so that you can see how they are related. Read the words in each group. Then write the name of the class to which the words belong.

Cities	Explorers	Machines	Transportation
Countryside	Fish	Ranch	Trees
Desert	Jungle	Storms	Waters

1. _____

catfish
herring
shark
trout

2. _____

astronaut
pioneer
scientists
scuba diver

3. _____

airplanes
buses
railroad
subway

4. _____

apartment buildings
parks
skyscrapers
traffic

5. _____

meadow
pasture
prairie
valley

6. _____

cattle
corral
cowhands
horses

7. _____

hail
hurricane
rain
thunder

8. _____

cobra
monkeys
parrot
vines

9. _____

birch
cottonwood
elm
spruce

10. _____

canal
bay
lake
river

11. _____

computer
dryer
typewriter
vacuum cleaner

12. _____

cactus
lizards
rattlesnake
sand dunes

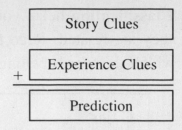
Predicting Outcomes

When you read a story and guess what will happen next, you are making a **prediction.** Making predictions is a good way to help you understand what you read. To make a prediction, use clues in the story and what you know about events that are like those in the story.

Story Clues
Experience Clues
Prediction

A. Read the story. Write a prediction and the story clues that helped you make the prediction. Then read on to see what really did happen.

> Remember that predictions must make sense with a story.

It was the day of the school concert. Billy had been looking forward to this day. He felt that his flute sang to him when he played it. He hoped that other people would feel that way too. As the principal greeted the audience, Billy felt his stomach flutter. He was a bit nervous. But he had practiced a lot, and he felt that he was ready.

1. Prediction: _____

_____

2. Story clues: _____

_____

_____

When Billy's turn came, he stepped forward, lifted his flute, and started to play. At first he was nervous, but after a few seconds he relaxed. Then he made his flute seem to sing, just as he wanted it to.

B. Think of what you know about the things that happened in the story. Write the experience clues that helped you make your prediction.

_____

_____

_____

_____

Long Word Decoding

When you read long words, use what you know about word parts and about syllables to figure out how to pronounce the word. Follow these rules:

1. Look for words or word parts you know. (*raincoat, unevenly*)

2. Divide what is left into syllables. (e ven)

3. Say each part slowly.

4. Try out different vowel sounds. (meet, ten, open)

A. Sort the words into the boxes. Use what you know about decoding compound words and decoding words with prefixes and suffixes. Then circle the two words in each compound word you wrote. In the other box, underline each prefix once and underline each suffix twice.

boxcar	fanciful	outpost	valuable
chairlift	harmless	replacement	woodland
disappearing	masterpiece	uneasiness	wristwatch

Compound Words

_____

_____

_____

_____

_____

Prefixes and Suffixes

_____

_____

_____

_____

_____

B. Add *-ly, -est,* or *-ed* to these words to make new words: *noisy, repeat, incorrect, unhappy*.

1. _____   3. _____

2. _____   4. _____

Context Clues

To figure out the meaning of an unfamiliar word, look at the other words and sentences around the word. This is called using context clues. Read the example.

Example: It would be impossible to count all the stars in a <u>galaxy</u> as large as the Milky Way.

The words that come before and after *galaxy* help you to understand that a galaxy is a vast, or very great, group of stars.

Read the sentences. Use context clues to decide which word from the box makes sense in each sentence. Then write that word.

| constellation | gathered | meteor | telescope |
| frustrated | horizon | spotted | windowpane |

1. One clear winter night, Denny wanted to watch the sky. He took out his new

   _____ .

2. First he tried looking at the stars through a window, but the

   _____ was dirty and streaked.

3. Then he aimed lower, at the _____ . There he saw just the
   tops of the buildings in his city.

4. Denny sighed deeply. He felt _____ that he could find no
   interesting sights.

5. Denny thought about what to do. Then he _____ that the
   only way to get a good view was to open the window.

6. "Maybe now I can see a _____ like the Big Dipper,"
   Denny said to himself.

7. Suddenly a white flash against the darkness surprised him. Was it a

   _____ speeding across the sky?

8. Denny found the biggest, brightest object in the sky. "At last I've

   _____ a planet!" he exclaimed.

Vocabulary: Story Critical Words

A. Study the meaning of each word.

afford   to have enough money to pay for

bargain   to try to get the best price

chores   tasks

eagerly   with enthusiasm

quivered   shook slightly; trembled

snatched   grabbed

stump   the part of a tree left after the tree has been cut down

trembling   shaking; quivering

B. Sometimes the meaning of a word is given in a clue that is almost an example. Read each sentence clue. Then write the correct word in the puzzle.

Across

3. What you do to buy something cheaply.

5. Only this part of the tree remained after lightning hit it.

7. If you save enough money, you can do this for things you'd like to have.

8. The leaves did this in the breeze.

Down

1. The robber did this to the diamond necklace.

2. The people watching the movie were doing this during a very scary part of the film.

4. These are small jobs you do around the house.

6. This is how you might open a present.

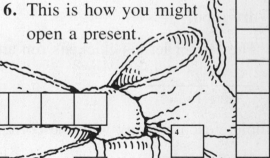

Vocabulary: Support Words

A. Study the meaning of each word.

barnyard ground near a barn
bundle things bound together
calico a cotton cloth with small colored designs
dens places where wild animals live

lantern a glass case that holds light
shapeless without a definite shape
strapped fastened with a strap or rope
thaw to melt

B. Finish each sentence with the correct vocabulary word.

1. During winter, bears sleep in their _____ .

2. The ranger lit her _____ to see into the dark cave.

3. The snow will _____ when the weather warms up.

4. Lisa's dress was made of _____ .

5. Dad _____ the suitcase to the top of the car.

6. Bill carried a _____ of clothes to the laundry room.

7. The farmer let his chickens run around the _____ .

C. Complete each analogy with the correct vocabulary word.

8. *Odd* is to *even* as *shapely* is to _____ .

9. *Nests* are to *birds* as _____ are to *wolves*.

10. *Lifted* is to *raised* as *tied* is to _____ .

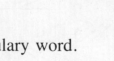

D. Write the vocabulary word each sentence tells about.

11. These can be caves or holes dug into the ground. _____

12. Ice cubes will do this if you put them in hot water. _____

13. You might take this along when you go camping. _____

Alphabetical Order

Words in **alphabetical order** are listed in the order of the letters of the alphabet. For example, these words are in alphabetical order: *sun, sunbeam, Sunday, sunflower*. To alphabetize words, put them in order by looking at the first, second, third, and fourth letters. Knowing alphabetical order will help you to find words in a dictionary, an encyclopedia, a telephone directory, and a card catalog.

A. Write the words in each list in alphabetical order.

1. citron _____

    citrate _____

    citrous _____

    citrus _____

    citrine _____

3. hangnail _____

    hanger _____

    hangout _____

    hangar _____

    hanging _____

2. eyebrow _____

    eyelid _____

    eyeball _____

    eyelash _____

    eye _____

4. coat _____

    coal _____

    color _____

    coast _____

    cold _____

B. These words are in alphabetical order. Mark an **X** where you would add each new word.

5. trumpet

    trundle

    truth

Where would you put **trust**?

7. act

    action

    actor

Where would you put **actin**?

6. pickle

    picnic

    pictorial

Where would you put **picture**?

8. sauce

    saucer

    sausage

Where would you put **saunter**?

Context Clues

Context clues help you figure out the meaning of unfamiliar words and of familiar words used in new ways. To figure out the meanings of words you do not know, look for clues before and after the word and in surrounding sentences.

Read the story. Use context clues to figure out which word from the box makes sense in each blank. Write those words.

backpack	cliff	head	panic	sharp
breathless	containers	hikers	relieved	sight
certain	farther	narrowed	route	welcome

Matt and Aleia were tired and _____ after climbing up the

steep hillside. They had lost _____ of Mr. Bell and the rest

of the _____ . But Aleia was _____ that

she and Matt could catch up to them. Matt started to run. His heavy

_____ slowed him down. Were they lost? The path had been

wide, but now it _____ as they reached the top of the hill.

When they had gone a little _____ , Matt said, "Oh, no!" He

could see that the path ended at the edge of a _____ . There was

no way to go but back down the same _____ .

Aleia said, "Let's not _____ . We must have taken a wrong

turn. The rest of the group cannot be too far away."

The two tired climbers sipped some water from their plastic

_____ . Then, as they began to _____ back

down the hill, they heard a _____ whistle and loud shouts.

"It's our group!" cried Matt.

Mr. Bell and the rest of the climbers gave them a big _____ .

Aleia and Matt were _____ that all they had missed was lunch.

© Silver, Burdett & Ginn Inc.

Classification

Words can be **classified,** or grouped together, according to the ways that they are alike. The whole group of words is often called a category or a class.

Complete the word map for Pets. Then add words of your own to the map.

aquarium	fish	leash	rabbit
bark	fly	meow	scamper
bowl	food	parakeet	splash
chirp	hop	peep	swim
collar	kitten	puppy	wriggle

1. Types of Pets

_____

_____

_____

_____

_____

3. Pet Sounds

_____

_____

_____

_____

_____

Pets

2. Pet Supplies

_____

_____

_____

_____

_____

4. Pet Movements

_____

_____

_____

_____

_____

Suffixes -*en*, -*ous*

Recognizing suffixes can help you understand the meanings of words and build your vocabulary. Read the examples and notice what the suffixes mean.

Examples: silk + -*en* = silken, "made of silk"

           bright + -*en* = brighten, "cause to be bright"

           joy + -*ous* = joyous, "having the qualities of joy"

           fury + -*ious* = furious, "having the qualities of fury"

A. Complete each sentence with the correct word. Write it.

1. The wizard held his _____ staff high.

     fallen   oaken   oakous

2. Because the area was _____ , walking was tiring.

     mountainous   glamorous   victorious

3. The zookeeper told them that the snake with the dark spots was

                                 _____ .

         wooden   poisonous   conscious

4. They had to _____ the butter to make the cookies.

     lighten   darken   soften

5. Manny felt worn out after finishing the _____ task.

     laborious   victorious   spacious

6. Thick _____ socks keep a hiker's feet dry.

     olden   wooden   woolen

7. Everyone thought Bev was _____ for climbing to the top of the rope in gym.

     gracious   courageous   famous

8. Ms. Bowker opened the windows to _____ the air.

     freshen   soften   furious

B. On separate paper, write the words that go with these meanings: "made of wood," and "cause to be dark." Then use each word in a sentence.

Comparison

A **comparison** shows how two or more things are alike and different. Words like *all*, *both*, *alike*, *similar*, *different*, *but*, *however*, and *whereas* often signal comparisons.

Example: <u>Both</u> jazz and opera are kinds of music. Jazz started in America. Opera began in Italy. Opera has long been popular, <u>but</u> jazz is modern.

Read the paragraphs. Complete the chart with **+** (yes) and **−** (no) signs. Answer the questions.

Soccer, baseball, and football are three sports that use special kinds of balls. All three sports have teams of players, and all three are played on large fields. Soccer and football fields are rectangles. A baseball field, however, has a baseball diamond.

Soccer players kick a round ball along the ground toward a goal net. Football players kick and pass a football in the air and run it toward a goal post. Baseball players bat and catch a baseball and run bases.

The three sports are alike in one way. Most teams have championship play offs. Major soccer teams compete for the World Cup. A major league baseball team wins the World Series. The country's two best football teams play in the Super Bowl.

	Baseball	Football	Soccer
catch and bat ball			
championship play-offs			
kick ball along ground			
run, pass, kick ball			
team of players			

1. How are football and soccer fields different from a baseball field?

_____

_____

2. Which of the three sports use goals, and how are the goals different?

_____

_____

Vocabulary: Story Critical Words

A. Study the meaning of each word.

averages has as an average, or middle
  amount

caution to warn

distinctive unusual

enable to make able

harm to hurt or damage

notches cuts in the form of a *V*

species a group of plants or animals that are
  alike in certain ways

suction a drawing of air out of a space

B. Read the paragraph. Complete each unfinished sentence with the correct
vocabulary word.

    Jim and Rick took a walk into the forest to look at birds. They took along a book

on birds. This book had information and pictures of all the different

_____ of birds that lived in the area.

    "I should _____ you to walk very quietly and carefully,"

Jim whispered to Rick. "We don't want to frighten away any birds or

_____ any of the plants!"

    The first bird they saw was a noisy woodpecker. It was pecking at a tree trunk,

making _____ in the wood. Suddenly, a small red bird darted

in front of them. Rick guessed that it might be a cardinal because of its

_____ coloring.

    "I think a cardinal's height _____ eight inches," said Jim,

"but that bird was smaller. We should look up the bird in our book. That will

_____ us to find out what kind of bird it was."

C. Write the word each sentence tells about.

1. You might make these in a belt to create a nice design. _____

2. Lightning that hits a tree might do this to it. _____

3. You do this when you tell someone to look both ways before crossing the street.

_____

4. A vacuum cleaner uses this to pick up dirt. _____

Vocabulary: Support Words

A. Study the meaning of each word.

blotched spotted	**grizzled** gray or streaked with gray
blunted dulled; no longer sharp	**hatch** to come out from the egg
captured caught	**rarely** not often, seldom
defense protection against attack	**vegetation** plant life

B. Finish each sentence with the correct vocabulary word. Write the word in the puzzle.

Across

3. The cat's fur was _____.

7. A forest has many different kinds of _____.

8. Eating healthy foods is a good _____ against illness.

Down

1. The police _____ the criminal.

2. The paper was _____ with spilled ink.

4. It _____ rains in the desert.

5. The knife was _____ by misuse.

6. The ducklings will _____ soon.

C. Write the correct vocabulary word to complete each analogy.

9. *Forever* is to *always* as *seldom* is to _____.

10. *Straight* is to *crooked* as *sharpened* is to _____.

11. *Cleaned* is to *dirtied* as *freed* is to _____.

12. *Closed* is to *shut* as *stained* is to _____.

Test-Taking

Learning how to organize your study materials and how to answer different kinds
of questions will help you take tests.

> **Guidelines for Test-Taking**
> ◆ Read statements carefully.
> ◆ Follow the directions exactly when you answer.
> ◆ Answer things you are sure of first.
> ◆ Check your answers.

Completion

A. Write **all** or **most** to correctly complete the sentences about multiple-choice tests.

1. Read _____ of the answer choices before you choose an answer.

2. _____ tests are multiple-choice.

True-False

B. Circle **T** if the sentence is **true.** Circle **F** if the sentence is **false.**

3. Study in a quiet, comfortable place with good lighting.   T   F

4. Stay up late on the night before the test.   T   F

Matching

C. Draw a line from the beginning of each sentence to the part that completes it correctly.

5. When you take a test,   follow the directions exactly.
6. After you take a test,   check your work.

Multiple-Choice

D. Read each question. Circle the letter of the best answer.

7. When should you organize your study materials for a test?
   a. before you study   **b.** while you study   **c.** after you study

8. What should you do after you finish taking a test?
   a. read the directions   **b.** look at your notes   **c.** check your answers

Comparison

A **comparison** shows how two or more things, people, events, or stories are alike or different. Sometimes words like *all, both, alike, similar, but, however,* and *different* signal a comparison.

A. Read the story. Then answer the questions about comparisons.

The three children disagreed on where to go for the family's vacation. Frankie wanted to visit Arizona. Martin also wanted to see the Southwest. He wanted to go to New Mexico. Their sister Sandra said that she would like to go to the beach. After a family discussion, they agreed on a trip to Arizona.

Each of the children had some money saved for the trip. Both Sandra and Martin decided to buy a piece of pottery. Their parents purchased postcards to send. Frankie bought a silver buckle for his belt.

All the Porters enjoyed the visit to the Grand Canyon. Martin liked taking pictures best of all. However, Sandra's favorite activity was taking a helicopter ride over the Grand Canyon. What Frankie enjoyed most were the fantastic colors.

1. How are Frankie and Martin alike in where they wanted to go?

_____

_____

2. How are Frankie and Martin different in where they wanted to go?

_____

_____

3. How is Frankie different from Martin and Sandra in what he bought?

_____

_____

4. How are the children different in what they enjoyed most about the Grand Canyon?

_____

_____

B. Underline the story sentences that tell how all the Porters are alike in some way.

Index

Sometimes the best way to find certain information in a book is to use the index at the back of the book. An **index** is an alphabetical list of the topics covered in the book and the pages on which these topics appear. A person's name is listed in the index with the last name first. Notice the parts of the index in the example.

main topic ⟶ Mars, 20

McDivitt, James, 13 ⟵ page numbers

Moon, 12-15

subtopic ⟶ mapping of, 15*m* ⟵ map reference

size of, 12

Use the information in the sample index to answer the questions.

INDEX

Earth, 9–18
   distance from sun, 11
   mapping of, 18*m*
   motion of, 10
   size of, 9, 17

Eclipses, 19, 44

Einstein, Albert, 22–23

Energy, 25–27
   solar, 26

Exploration, 46–51
   of atmosphere, 46
   of space, 47, 50–51

---

1. What page gives information about solar energy? _____

2. Which main topic tells you that there is information about our planet in this book?

_____

3. On what page could you find out how far the earth is from the sun? _____

4. Does this book contain information on space exploration? _____

5. What pages tell about the scientist Albert Einstein? _____

6. What page describes the earth's motion? _____

7. Where would you expect to find a map of the earth? _____

8. Where would you find facts about eclipses? _____

Main Idea/Details

The **main idea** tells what the paragraph is about. All the **details** should support the main idea. When a main idea is *not* stated, think of a sentence that tells about all the details.

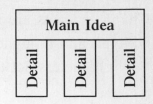

Main Idea		
Detail	Detail	Detail

> A main idea that is stated may be at the beginning, middle, or end of a paragraph.

A. Read each paragraph. Underline the main idea.

1.   People spread ideas and information in many ways. Newspaper reporters write about local, national, or world news. Weather reporters give information about the weather. People who write stories for books and magazines communicate their ideas to millions of people. People who write letters to friends and relatives also spread ideas.

2.   Fill a balloon with air. Let the balloon go before you tie it. The air inside the balloon will rush out. As the air rushes out of one end of the balloon, the other end moves forward —like a jet. The balloon seems to ''fly'' through the air. This balloon experiment shows you how some jet planes fly.

B. Read the paragraph. Select the main idea, and then write it.

3.   Every day you should eat some kind of bread or cereal. Fruits and vegetables provide your body with many of the vitamins it needs. Dairy products, like milk and cheese, are important for a well-balanced diet. A balanced diet usually includes meat, fish, or eggs, too.

Main Idea: _____

_____

Most bread is made from wheat or rye.
It is important to eat a good breakfast every day.
It is important to eat foods from all the different food groups.

© Silver, Burdett & Ginn Inc.

Characterization

Character traits are special qualities of personality. They can be seen in the speech, actions, and thoughts of a character. Understanding them will help a reader know why characters act the way they do and predict how characters will behave.

Read the story about Jerry. As you read, think about his character traits. Then answer the questions.

Jerry is usually very thoughtful. He often runs errands for his neighbors. He helps Mrs. North weed her garden. He walks Mr. Jefferson's dog twice a day. Today Jerry had a problem. He looked up at the kitchen clock and frowned when he saw the time.

"The basketball game with the kids starts in fifteen minutes, but I promised Grandma I'd get the listening tape for her," Jerry groaned. He didn't want to let his grandmother or his friends down. "Well," he said, "a promise is a promise!" Then he dashed out the door.

Jerry ran to the library to pick up the listening tape of one of his grandmother's favorite books and delivered it to her. Then he ran around the corner to the playground. When Jerry met his friends, they were just beginning to choose the teams.

1. How do you know that Jerry likes to keep his promises?

   _____

   _____

2. What did Jerry do to make sure that he kept his promise to his grandmother?

   _____

   _____

3. What does Jerry do that shows he is thoughtful?

   _____

   _____

4. How do you think Jerry felt when he saw what time it was? Circle the word that best describes his feeling.

   scared   discouraged   concerned

5. Which word best describes Jerry, as he is shown in the story? Circle the word.

   dependable   forgetful   fun-loving

Cause/Effect

A **cause** is an event or an action that results in another event or action called an **effect**. Sometimes words like *because, so,* and *therefore* signal cause-effect relationships. When clue words are not used, think about what happened and about how or why it happened. The cause and effect in the example has no clue word.

Cause → Effect

Example: ⌐—— cause ——⌐ ⌐—— effect ——⌐ Bonnie forgot to wear her gloves. Now her hands feel very cold.

Read each paragraph. Think about the causes and their effects. Then write the missing cause or effect.

1.   In 1848 gold was discovered in California. Thousands of people went there to start mining. Because gold was hard to find, it was very valuable. Even today gold jewelry is expensive. Mines are dug miles under the earth. There, deep under-ground, miners can find the gold that is later made into jewelry.

Cause: In 1848 gold was discovered in California.

Effect: _____

Cause: _____

Effect: Miners can find the gold that is later made into jewelry.

2.   Luke thought that panning for gold would be fun. With his father, he looked for a stream where they could try it. Luke dunked his pan in the water and lifted it. He scooped up some gravel and pebbles. As he moved the pan, the water and pebbles swirled. He looked for shiny bits of gold. After an hour of hard work, Luke decided to stop. But he didn't really want to give up yet. He tried panning one last time. Suddenly he saw a tiny gold flake sparkle in the pan and called to his father.

Cause: _____

Effect: Luke scooped up some gravel and pebbles.

Cause: Luke didn't really want to give up.

Effect: _____

Vocabulary: Story Critical Words

A. Study the meaning of each word.

climate   an area that has particular weather conditions

composed   calm, peaceful

festival   a special celebration

native   born in a certain country

original   first

parakeet   a small parrot

resolved   decided

B. Write the vocabulary word each sentence describes.

1. People enjoy themselves when they attend this. _____

2. This can be warm, cold, wet, or dry. _____

3. A person who acts this way is pleasant to be around. _____

4. This can be a plant or an animal at home in a certain place. _____

5. This pet often lives in a cage in people's houses. _____

C. One word in each sentence below does not make sense. Circle that word. Then write the vocabulary word that should go there.

6. In winter, ducks fly south to be in a warmer hotel. _____

7. A relaxing walk beside the lake always makes her feel supposed. _____

8. The school held a music popsicle. _____

9. The bald eagle is a naughty bird of North America. _____

10. Paul advertised to study and do well on the test. _____

D. Finish each sentence with the correct vocabulary word.

11. The _____ in Florida is usually warm throughout the year.

12. Tim's band played at the music _____.

13. Agnes likes to teach her _____ to do tricks.

14. Mr. Fu is a _____ of China.

15. The building was the _____ one on that site.

16. Joe was _____ as he prepared to give his speech.

17. Dulcy _____ to take her vacation in the summer.

Vocabulary: Support Words

A. Study the meaning of each word.

accustomed   made familiar with use or habit
advertised   announced publicly
earnings   money earned
flustered   excited or confused
matchmaker   a person who arranges marriages for others

plumage   a bird's feathers
prism   a glass object that breaks light into colors
theater   a place where plays and movies are shown

B. Finish each analogy with the correct vocabulary word.

1. *Fur* is to *bear* as _____ is to *peacock*.

2. *Concert hall* is to *music* as _____ is to *movie*.

3. *Sad* is to *happy* as _____ is to *composed*.

4. *Old* is to *new* as _____ is to *strange*.

C. Read about each situation. Write the vocabulary word that goes with it.

5. A company wanted to let people know about their newest video games. This is what they did. _____

6. During summer vacation, Abby works at the library. This is what she gets paid for her work. _____

7. Maggie wanted to make a rainbow on her wall. This is what she hung in the window. _____

D. Answer each question.

8. Which vocabulary word is made up of two smaller words? Write the word and draw a line (/) between the two smaller words. _____

9. How do the two smaller words create the meaning of the large word?

_____

_____

_____

Newspaper

Everything in a newspaper answers *who, what, where,* and *when.* In a news article, the most important information usually appears in the first paragraph. This paragraph is called the **lead.** The **index** shows where the major sections are located. Read the newspaper article and the index. Then answer the questions.

Morning Edition   **The Daily Bulletin**   Today's Weather: Rain

No. 92   Newtowne, March 2   15 cents

MIDDLETOWN   Several members of the 50-Plus Community Preservation Club warned Middletown residents of a flash flood early this morning.

Out on a survey of wildlife damage from the recent heavy rains, the club members saw the flood coming. They radioed their home

base. The people of Middletown were immediately notified. Soon thereafter, the weather service also issued a warning.

The 50-Plus Club members were thanked by TV news reporters for their quick thinking. ''We believe that many injuries were avoided due to their timely warning,'' one reporter said.

The weather service also issued an official message of thanks for the club's valuable assistance.

Two 50-Plus club members help with flood warning.

INDEX

Comics 15
Editorials 7
Entertainment 13
News 1
Sports 18
Weather 4

---

1. Write these important facts from the lead. Where: _____

   Who: _____

   What: _____   When: _____

2. Write a headline for the article that highlights the information in the lead.

   _____

3. Where should the headline appear? _____

4. From the index, write the pages on which you would find the following information: the weather forecast _____ movie times _____ big game scores _____

Cause/Effect

In some stories cause-effect relationships are signaled by words like *because*, *since*, *therefore*, *so*, or *as a result*. Some stories do not use signal words.

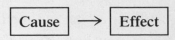

Read each paragraph. Answer the questions. Then underline the cause-effect signal words in the paragraph.

Angelica pounded and kneaded the large block of clay. The clay became soft. She spread the soft clay into a thick square. Her hands became sticky and gray. Since she needed a model to follow, she looked in her book. Angelica shaped the clay into buildings of different sizes. Her clay village began to grow.

1. Why did Angelica pound and knead the clay? _____

_____

2. Why were Angelica's hands sticky and gray? _____

_____

3. Why did Angelica make buildings of different sizes?

_____

In the early Southwest, wood, stone, and other building materials were scarce, but there was plenty of clay. Therefore, many people built their homes of clay. The red clay was gathered and shaped into bricks. Then the clay bricks were dried in the sun. As a result, the bricks became hard enough for builders to use. Clay bricks kept the heat out of buildings and kept the air inside cool. Homes made from these bricks were excellent shelters.

4. Why were early Southwest homes made of clay? _____

_____

5. What was the effect of drying bricks in the sun? _____

_____

6. Why were these homes excellent shelters? _____

_____

Inference

Sometimes an author does not tell you every detail in a story.
Then you have to make inferences. To make an inference, use
the clues in the story and clues based on your own experience.

Story Clues
+ Experience Clues
Inference

A. Read the story. Answer the questions. For questions 2–4,
write the story clues that helped you make the inferences.

Abby was curled up in her seat. Suddenly the whistle blew. Abby woke up and
blinked her eyes. As she sat up, she could hear the squeaking and grinding of the
wheels. Then she glanced out of the dusty window. She saw two girls standing on the
other side of the railroad crossing, smiling and waving, and she smiled back at them.
Then the small town and its shops slowly disappeared.

Just then, a kindly man stopped at her seat and asked, "Miss, could I have your
ticket, please?" Abby handed him her ticket.

She watched for a moment as he moved along to the next seats. A young boy
blocked his path. He was trying to put what he was carrying onto the overhead rack.
Then Abby sat back and enjoyed the scenes that seemed to speed by her.

1. Where was Abby? _____
Underline the parts of the story that gave you clues for answering this question.

2. What was Abby doing just before the whistle blew? _____

Story clues: _____

3. Who were the two girls probably waving at? _____

Story clues: _____

4. Who was the person that spoke to Abby? Circle the answer.

the young boy   the conductor   a friend

Story clues: _____

_____

B. On separate paper, write the clues from your own experience that helped you answer
each question.

Predicting Outcomes

When you read a story and guess what will happen next, you are making a prediction. As you read, use clues in the story and what you already know about events like those in the story to make a prediction.

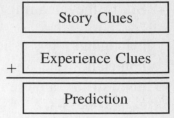

Read each little story. Circle two possible predictions for each one.

1. Stanley is asleep. He wakes up. It is very late. Stanley looks out the window and sees a house on fire. What do you think Stanley will do?

He will wake up his parents.

He will go back to sleep.

He will call the fire department.

2. Donna is very fair. One day she finds a lot of money on a bus. What do you think Donna will do?

She will give the money to the driver.

She will leave the money on the bus.

She will try to find out who lost it.

3. James is alone in a cabin. He is watching TV. His friends are swimming in the lake nearby. James hears that a bad storm is coming. What do you think James will do?

He will watch TV.

He will shut all the windows.

He will try to get his friends out of the lake.

He will get out the battery for his TV.

4. David climbs to the top of the roof of his house. He is afraid to climb down. He sees Mrs. McGinnis and starts to wave and yell. What do you think will happen?

Mrs. McGinnis will bring a ladder and David will climb down.

Mrs. McGinnis will call the fire department.

Mrs. McGinnis will wave and yell hello.

5. Carmelita wants a pet. Her mother and father say she can't have one. A friend gives Carmelita a garden snake. She hides the snake in the bathtub. Carmelita's mother wants to take a bath. What do you think will happen?

Carmelita's mother and father may be angry when they see the snake.

Carmelita's mother will take a bath.

Carmelita's mother or father will take the snake to the woods.

Carmelita's mother and father will buy Carmelita a dog for her birthday.

Vocabulary: Story Critical Words

A. Study the meaning of each word.

belongings   possessions
homeland   the country where one is born
homestead   a piece of public land given to a
settler to farm

journey   a trip
nuisance   a person or thing that causes
trouble
settlement   a small village

B. Finish each sentence with the correct vocabulary word.

1. My friend Pia's _____ is Italy.

2. Loud music is a _____ when you're trying to study.

3. The pioneer family traveled westward to settle on their new _____.

4. They made the _____ in a covered wagon.

5. They took all their _____ with them.

C. Write the vocabulary word that answers each question.

6. Which two words contain the same word?

_____   _____

7. What do movers pack for people when they move? _____

8. What place is a small community of people? _____

9. What could you call a person or thing that bothers you? _____

D. Answer the question.

10. What journey would you like to take? Where would you like to go, and why?
How would you like to make the journey—by car, train, plane, boat, or
spacecraft?

_____

_____

_____

_____

_____

Vocabulary: Support Words

A. Study the meaning of each word.

clearing   making empty or clear
hold   the storage area below the deck of a ship
oxcart   a cart pulled by oxen

pitched   tossed about, as a boat on rough water
shaft   one of the two poles between which an animal is harnessed to a wagon
shores   the land at the edge of water

B. Some words can be classified together. Read each row of words. Cross out the word that does not belong. Then write the vocabulary word that fits the classification.

1. beaches   ships   coasts   _____

2. wagon   carriage   read   _____

3. people   basket   container   _____

4. shook   slapped   still   _____

C. Answer each question with the correct vocabulary word.

5. Which two words have to do with a ship or with what happens to ships?

_____   _____

6. Which two words have to do with wagons pulled by animals?

_____   _____

7. Which word can refer to what a person does to a table or a piece

of wooded land?   _____

D. Read the following paragraph. Finish each incomplete sentence with the correct vocabulary word.

There was a huge storm at sea. The fishing boat was _____ by great waves. Men were busy _____ the deck of loose things that might be swept away by the storm. Crates of fish stored in the _____ of the boat were sliding and crashing into the walls. The captain hoped the boat would survive the storm and safely reach the _____ .

Figurative Language

Figurative language is a way of putting words together to paint a picture in a reader's mind. By recognizing figurative language you can see how writers describe things in a vivid and imaginative way.

> Examples: **Simile:** The polished <u>pan</u> gleams <u>like a new penny</u>.
> **Metaphor:** The <u>jumprope</u> on the ground <u>was a coiled snake</u>.
> **Idiom:** Karen's bright jacket <u>caught my eye</u>.
> **Exaggeration:** That basketball player <u>could reach the top of a skyscraper!</u>

A **simile** compares two different things using the words *like* or *as*. A **metaphor** compares two different things, using the words *is, are, was,* or *were*. An **idiom** is an expression that uses words in a special way so that their meanings are different. **Exaggeration** stretches the truth to make a point.

A. Draw lines between the two parts of a sentence that make a vivid comparison.

1. Thunder during a fierce storm is   tiny pieces of lace.
2. The bar of soap smelled as sweet as   a rocket blast.
3. Snowflakes on a window look like   fresh roses.

B. Write one of these idioms to complete each sentence: *fell flat, hit the ceiling,* or *caught his breath*.

4. After the steep climb, Wes stopped and _____ .

5. Mr. Wright was so angry that he _____ .

6. Toby's plans for a picnic _____ when it rained.

C. Write *everything in sight* or *a small crumb* to complete each sentence with exaggeration.

7. I am so full that I cannot eat even _____ .

8. Pat was so hungry that she could eat _____ .

D. Write an example of figurative language of your own.

_____

_____

_____

Choosing Among Resources

You can use **resources**, or reference sources, in the library to answer questions or find information about a topic. If you know what each resource contains, you will be able to choose the best one to locate the information you need.

1. A **card or computer catalog** lists all the books in a library in alphabetical order by the title and the author's last name. Nonfiction books are also listed by subject.

2. A **dictionary** is an alphabetical list of words. Each entry tells how to spell the word, how to pronounce it, and what it means.

3. An **encyclopedia** is a set of books. Each volume contains articles arranged alphabetically by topic. Each article tells the most important facts about the topic.

4. A **newspaper** gives up-to-date information about daily events.

5. A **telephone directory** includes yellow pages that list types of businesses and services alphabetically.

Which resource would you use to find the answer to each question?

1. What is Vega Oil Company's phone number? _____

2. What does the word *fossil* mean? _____

3. When was oil first discovered in the North Sea? _____

4. How is oil taken from the ground? _____

5. Who wrote *Conserving Fuels?* _____

6. What company repairs oil burners? _____

7. Where did yesterday's oil spill occur? _____

8. Does the library have a book on oil wells? _____

9. How do you pronounce the word *petroleum*? _____

10. When does the TV program on oil rigs start? _____

11. Where does Barbara Hathaway live? _____

12. When do wild ducks migrate? _____

13. Where did the word *gnarled* come from? _____

Cause/Effect

A **cause** is an event or an action that results in another event or action, called an **effect.**

| Cause | → | Effect |

A. Read each paragraph. Match the cause and effect statements.
Write the letter of the effect next to its cause.

It was time to tame the young wild horse for riding. Paula put a saddle on the horse. Because it was not used to the feel of a saddle, the horse was afraid. It ran around the big ring. Paula held the rope firmly. She made sure the young horse did not run away. All this time, Paula spoke gently to the horse so that it would calm down and learn to trust her.

Cause

1. _____ Paula spoke gently to the horse.

2. _____ The horse was not used to the saddle.

3. _____ Paula held the rope firmly.

Effect

a. The horse was afraid and ran around the ring.

b. Paula made sure the horse did not run away.

c. The horse would calm down and learn to trust her.

Camels are strong animals. They can carry heavy loads for many miles across dry lands. People who live in the desert have always valued camels. They can ride them and use them to move goods from one place to another. Because camels can survive with little to eat or drink, desert travel is easy for these animals.

Cause

4. _____ Camels are strong animals.

5. _____ People who live in the desert value camels.

6. _____ Camels can survive with little to eat or drink.

Effect

a. Desert travel is easy for camels.

b. Camels can carry heavy loads for many miles.

c. People can ride camels and use them to move goods.

B. On separate paper, write two sentences showing cause-effect relationships. Use a signal word in one of the sentences.

Context Clues

Context clues help you figure out the meaning of unfamiliar words. Sometimes writers give you a context clue that tells the meaning of a word right in the sentence.

Read the example. Notice that the meaning of the underlined word is in the sentence.

Example: <u>Geology,</u> the study of the earth, helps explain how the land is formed.

Read each sentence. Figure out the meaning of the underlined word by finding its definition in the sentence. Then write the definition.

1. The Grand Canyon was formed by <u>erosion</u>, the wearing away of rock by wind, water, or ice.

   _____

2. For millions of years a river carved a deep <u>canyon</u>, or valley with steep sides, from layers of rock.

   _____

3. Rain water can wear down rock to leave <u>pillars</u>, or tall columns of stone.

   _____

4. A moving sheet of ice called a <u>glacier</u> creates waterfalls and lakes as it melts.

   _____

5. The action of wind helps to shape the <u>mesas</u>, which are flat-topped mountains with steep sides.

   _____

6. Rock is also <u>abraded</u>, or worn away, by sand that blows against it.

   _____

7. Over centuries our landscape is slowly <u>altered</u>, or changed.

   _____

Sequence

The events in a story happen in a certain order called **sequence.** Words like *first*, *next*, *after*, *then*, *later*, and *finally* signal the sequence. Sometimes two or more events happen at the same time. Words like *during*, *as*, *when*, and *while* signal events that happen at the same time.

| Event | → | then | → | Event |

| Event | ← | while | → | Event |

A. Read the story. Then answer the questions. Use the time order clue words in the story to help you.

Juan was just about ready. He practiced his lines once more while he put on his costume. He adjusted his long robe. Next he placed the king's crown on his head. As Juan looked in the mirror, he heard his name called. It was time for the king to go on stage. While the king walked to the center of the stage, he waved and smiled. Then he gave a very important speech. Juan forgot only one line. After the curtain fell, the audience clapped. Finally, when Juan came out to take a bow, everyone cheered.

1. What did the king do while he walked to the center of the stage?

_____

2. What was the first thing the king did after he got to the center of the stage?

_____

3. What did Juan do while he was putting on his costume?

_____

4. What happened at the same time that Juan looked in the mirror?

_____

5. What did Juan do after he adjusted his long robe?

_____

6. What were the last two things that happened at the same time in the story?

_____

B. On separate paper, write two sentences that tell about something that might have happened next in the story. Use time order clue words to signal the sequence.

Forms of Poetry

Poetry has different forms. Two of these forms are narrative verse and free verse. **Narrative verse** tells a story and has repeated patterns of rhyming words and rhythm, or regular beats. **Free verse** has no regular pattern of rhyme and rhythm. By recognizing different forms of poetry, you can understand and appreciate them better.

The poems labeled **A** and **B** come from longer poems. Read each poem. Then answer the questions.

A

I measure myself
Against a tall tree.
I find that I am much taller,
For I reach right up to the sun,
With my eye;
And I reach to the shore of the sea
With my ear.
Nevertheless, I dislike
The way the ants crawl
In and out of my shadow.

—Wallace Stevens

B

Up and spoke an elderly knight,
  (Sat at the king's right knee),
"Sir Patrick Spence is the best sailor
  That sails upon the sea."

The king has written a broad letter,
  And signed it with his hand,
And sent it to Sir Patrick Spence,
  Was walking on the sand.

—Anonymous ballad,
  "Sir Patrick Spence"

1. In which poem, **A** or **B**, does a character tell about another character? _____

  Which character is speaking? _____

2. Write the lines from poem **A** that tell why the narrator ("I") seems to be taller than a tree.

  _____

  _____

  _____

  _____

3. Is Sir Patrick Spence a knight, a king, or a sailor? _____

4. Which poem is free verse, **A** or **B?** Give reasons for your answer. _____

  _____

Vocabulary: Story Critical Words

A. Study the meaning of each word.

admiring   looking at with wonder and delight
celebrate   to honor the memory of
celebrations   events that honor the memory
   of special things

exactly   in an exact, accurate way
lonely   feeling alone and unhappy
wandering   roaming; traveling aimlessly

B. Finish each sentence with the correct vocabulary word. Write the word in the puzzle.

Across

2. The town had planned many Fourth of July _____ .

4. The cat was _____ around the yard.

5. At the sound of the bell, it will be _____ 5 o'clock.

Down

1. Ann felt _____ at the new school until she made friends.

2. Let's _____ your birthday!

3. Dan was _____ Sue's beautiful painting.

C. Write the vocabulary word for each sentence clue.

6. You can do this on your birthday. _____

7. You might be doing this if you were looking at a beautiful object.

_____

8. People often have these on holidays. _____

9. When you add numbers, you should do it in this way. _____

10. You might be doing this in a park on a warm, sunny day.

_____

Vocabulary: Support Words

A. Study the meaning of each word.

coyote   a small North American wolf
drizzle   light, fine rain
triple   made up of three

B. Some words belong to the same classification. Read each row of words. Draw an **X** through the word that does not belong. Then write the vocabulary word that does belong.

1. umbrella   snow   rain   _____

2. lion   zoo   monkey   _____

3. count   single   double   _____

4. nine   twenty-seven   five   _____

C. Complete each sentence with the correct vocabulary word.

5. Stacy wore her raincoat to protect herself from the _____ .

6. The _____ howled throughout the night.

7. Stan likes spinach so much that he had a _____ portion.

8. I did not want to go out into the _____ without an umbrella.

9. The acrobat did a _____ handspring.

10. The _____ wandered around the open prairie.

D. Write a sentence for each vocabulary word.

11. coyote _____

_____

12. drizzle _____

_____

13. triple _____

_____

Charts

A **chart** or a **table** presents information in columns and rows. A **schedule** is a kind of chart that gives the times that events take place.

Study the bus schedule. Then answer the questions.

Speedy Lines Bus Schedule Fair River—Port City Schedule effective January 1, 1990				
Bus Number	Leave Fair River	Arrive Woodland	Leave Woodland	Arrive Port City
# 35	8:00 A.M.	8:35 A.M.	8:45 A.M.	9:00 A.M.
# 40	10:00 A.M.	10:35 A.M.	10:45 A.M.	11:00 A.M.
# 57	+12:10 P.M.	_____	_____	1:00 P.M.
# 101	* 3:20 P.M.	* 3:55 P.M.	* 4:05 P.M.	* 4:20 P.M.
+ No stops * Fridays only				

1. What is the title of the schedule? _____

2. Where do you get on the bus first? _____

3. What is the last stop the bus makes? _____

4. Where does the bus stop between Fair River and Port City? _____

5. Which buses travel between Fair River and Port City on Monday?

   _____

6. What time does bus #35 leave Fair River? _____

7. Which is the only nonstop bus between Fair River and Port City? _____

8. How many minutes do buses stop in Woodland? _____

9. Which bus would you take from Fair River to meet your grandparents in Port City

   at 4:30 on Friday? _____

Figurative Language

Figurative language is a special use of words. Writers may compare things that are alike in one way but different in every other way. Figurative language can help you see things in a new and exciting way. Read the examples of figurative language.

Examples: The old car moves like a giant turtle. (simile)

Uncle Milt is a ball of fire at family parties! (metaphor)

"You will have to pull your own weight," said the boss. (idiom)

My older brother has muscles of steel. (exaggeration)

A. Read the pairs of sentences. Then write the sentence that uses figurative language.

1. The airport was very busy and noisy.
The airport was like a busy hive of bees.

_____

2. The jet plane seemed to travel at the speed of light.
The jet plane was traveling at a high rate of speed.

_____

3. From high above, the fields were a patchwork quilt.
From high above, the fields were small squares of land.

_____

4. Riding in a car can't hold a candle to flying.
Riding in a car isn't nearly as much fun as flying.

_____

B. Choose a word or phrase to complete each sentence and write it.

angry ducks	pins and needles	sea of metal	snails

5. The cars crept along as slowly as _____ .

6. Vicky was on _____ waiting for the traffic to move.

7. The crowded street was a _____ .

8. The car horns sounded like _____ .

Multiple Meanings

A **multiple-meaning** word is a word that has more than one meaning. Context clues can often help you figure out which meaning is used. Read the examples.

Examples: A huge crowd filled the concert hall.
        Jeff tried to crowd his way onto the packed bus.

The word *crowd* in the first sentence means "a large group of people." In the second sentence, *crowd* means "to push or squeeze."

A. Read each pair of sentences. Then choose the meaning for each underlined word and write it. Use context clues to help you.

a movie	not common
a public area in a city, with	partly raw
streets on four sides	the symbol of a country,
having four equal sides	with certain colors and
material used for taking pictures	designs
	to become weak

1. Cindy and her dad visited an old <u>square</u> in Mexico City. _____

_____

   Cindy bought a <u>square</u> hand-woven rug. _____

2. Dad put <u>film</u> in his camera. _____

   At the museum, they saw a <u>film</u> on Old Mexico. _____

3. They also saw an exhibit of <u>rare</u> old coins. _____

   At lunch, Cindy didn't eat the <u>rare</u> steak. _____

4. Later, Cindy felt tired, but her spirits didn't <u>flag</u>. _____

   "Look, Dad! Isn't that the Mexican <u>flag</u>?" she asked. _____

B. Choose one pair of underlined words. On separate paper, write two sentences that show the two different meanings.

Cause/Effect

You sometimes find cause-effect relationships in stories to explain what happened and how or why events happened.

Cause → Effect

> Words like *if*, *because*, *therefore*, *so*, and *as a result* often signal cause-effect relationships.

Read the paragraphs. Then answer the questions.

Minnik lives in a land in the far north, where it snows most of the year. If he and his father go on a hunting trip, they make an igloo for shelter. Minnik helps his father cut and lift heavy chunks of ice to build the igloo.

Because there are two people working, the job goes faster. They place the cut blocks of ice in a circle. Then the add more blocks, making each row lean in. These blocks form the walls.

Finally, Minnik and his father add the last block of ice. Now the igloo has a roof. They use snow to fill in all the cracks. This will keep out the cold wind. Minnik also helps to line the walls inside with furs. The igloo is warm and cozy, even when the icy winds blow hard.

1. What makes the job of building the igloo go faster? _____

_____

2. Why is the igloo warm and cozy? _____

_____

3. Why do Minnik and his father make an igloo? _____

_____

4. Why do they add blocks of ice to the igloo? _____

_____

5. What is the effect of having all the cracks filled with snow? _____

_____

Vocabulary: Story Critical Words

A. Study the meaning of each word.

amuse   to entertain with humor
create   to make something new or original
overlap   to cover a part of something

patience   the ability to wait calmly without giving up
reflection   an image, as in a mirror
rib   a large vein in a leaf

B. Find and circle the six vocabulary words hidden in the puzzle. The words go in two directions, across and down. Write each word after you have circled it.

```
m  e  l  p  q  o  s  l  n  e  m
r  e  f  l  e  c  t  i  o  n  o
i  o  o  v  e  r  l  a  p  m  n
b  a  m  u  s  e  g  f  a  c  p
r  l  o  e  r  a  o  t  e  f  s
o  t  n  p  a  t  i  e  n  c  e
m  s  l  o  r  e  l  n  o  f  o
```

1. _____

2. _____

3. _____

4. _____

5. _____

6. _____

C. Finish each sentence with the correct vocabulary word.

7. The clown liked to _____ people with her tricks.

8. Everyone in class had to _____ a Halloween mask for the parade.

9. Because some of the shows at the festival _____ each other, we can't see them all.

10. You shouldn't give up if something doesn't happen right away. You should have _____ .

11. The water in the pond was so bright and calm that you could see your _____ in it.

Vocabulary: Support Words

A. Study the meaning of each word.

blossoms flowers, especially of a plant that bears fruit

fungi plants with no green color, leaves, or flowers, such as mushrooms

necklace a neck ornament, such as a string of beads

pods cases that hold plant seeds such as peas

seed-heads flowers' blossom parts that are full of seeds

strands things like threads or strings

supply the amount at hand

toadstools mushrooms, especially poisonous ones

tuft a bunch of small parts, such as hairs, held together at one end

B. Read the story. Complete each unfinished sentence with the correct vocabulary word. Write the words on the lines.

When dawn broke, the scout continued his journey through the rain forest. The vegetation was covered with a heavy dew, which made the delicate _____ droop with its weight. Light filtered through the branches, making the otherwise colorless _____ glisten. In the moist undergrowth, the scout could see many small _____. The scout bent down to study their umbrella shapes. He thought about picking one, but then remembered that they might be poisonous.

As he walked on, he almost tripped on a _____ of wet grass. The scout's hand shot out. He was lucky to grab some long _____ of a vine and avoid a dangerous fall. As he steadied himself, he bumped against some _____, scattering their dark blue seeds on the forest floor.

The scout had to make it through this difficult area of the forest before his food _____ ran out.

C. Answer each question.

1. Which five vocabulary words name things that grow?

_____

_____

2. Which two vocabulary words can name kinds of jewelry?

_____

Charts

Charts and tables present information in columns and rows. A schedule is a kind of chart that gives the times that events take place.

Use the movie schedule to answer the questions.

Starlight Movie Listings 419 Main Street March 1 - 7		
Movie	Day	Time
Cry of the Moon	Friday, Sunday	7:00, 9:00
Creature Features	Saturday	2:30
Life Is a Vacation	Monday, Saturday	3:55, *5:55, 7:55
Comedy Night	Tuesday, Wednesday	6:15, 8:15
Flight of the Eagle	Thursday	1:50, 7:50
Film Classics	Sunday	5:00
* Special discount on tickets		

1. What is the title of the schedule? _____

2. What movie plays at the Starlight on Monday? _____

3. What movie plays at the Starlight on both Friday and Sunday?

   _____

4. At what times does *Flight of the Eagle* start? _____

5. What movie is shown the most times this week? _____

6. On what evening can someone see a movie classic? _____

7. When can you see a movie at a special low price? _____

   _____

8. On what afternoon is a horror movie shown? _____

9. What kind of movie is shown on Tuesday or Wednesday night? _____

10. Which movie at the Starlight begins the latest? _____

Comparison

A **comparison** shows how two or more things, people, events, or stories are alike or different. Words like *both, alike, same, but, however,* and *different* sometimes signal comparisons.

A. Read the selection. Then complete the chart.

Lightning and swamp lights are two types of natural lights. Lightning appears in the sky, but swamp lights appear on the ground.

Swamp lights are colorful. They may shine yellow, blue, or red. However, a flash of lightning is white.

The two kinds of light have different forms. Lightning is a sudden streak or flash. Swamp lights look like tiny flames or fireballs.

Swamp lights and lightning are different in another way. Swamp lights are caused by gases given off by rotting plants. Lightning is caused by the electricity built up during a thunderstorm.

	Lightning	Swamp Lights
1. cause	electricity built up during thunderstorm	
2. color		
3. form		
4. location	sky	
5. type of light		natural

B. Write the comparison clue words used in the selection. Then, using one of those words, write a sentence about something you have seen in nature that makes a comparison.

_____

_____

_____

Following Directions

Directions are useful in telling you how to make something, how to get from one place to another, how to use a computer, and so on. In order to follow directions, you must know what steps to take and when to take each one.

The directions for making an ant house are out of order. Write the steps in the correct order. Use the direction words to help you.

How to Make an Ant House

You will need these materials to make an ant house. Then follow the steps.

dirt full of ants lid with holes punched
empty frozen juice can piece of black paper
empty glass jar two rubber bands

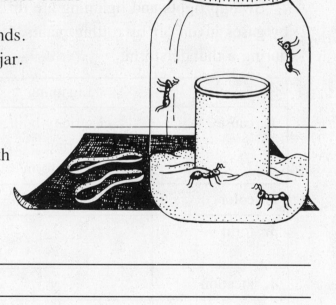

Hold the black paper in place with rubber bands.
First, place the juice can upside down in the jar.
After a few hours, remove the black paper.
Next, find an anthill of dirt full of ants.
Then put the lid back on the jar.
Fill the space between the jar and the can with the ant-filled dirt.
Finally, wrap black paper around the jar.

1. _____
2. _____
3. _____
   _____
4. _____
5. _____
6. _____
7. _____

When your ant house is completed, the ants will make paths and chambers in the dirt. You can feed the ants with drops of sweetened water and have fun watching them.

NAME _____

Figurative Language

Figurative language is descriptive writing that may include similes, metaphors, idioms, and exaggeration. Read the examples.

Examples: This lawn looks as dry as a desert. (simile)
The kites were graceful birds. (metaphor)
"Stop bugging me!" shouted Sam. (idiom)
The road seemed to go on forever. (exaggeration)

A. Read the story. Then follow the directions.

Before the concert, Ellen paced like a caged animal. The rest of the band was already on stage. When the curtain went up, Ellen was so nervous that she froze. Her hands were useless lumps of clay. "Could she make the grade?" she wondered.

Then Ellen performed the drum solo. The drum beats sounded like thunder. After the concert, the audience clapped so hard that the building shook. Later, Eddie said to Ellen, "See, I told you we would bring down the house."

Complete each sentence with a different comparison from the one in the paragraph.

1. Ellen paced like _____.

2. The drum beats sounded like _____.

3. Her hands were _____.

Write what each underlined idiom means.

4. Ellen wanted to <u>make the grade</u>. _____

5. The concert <u>brought down the house.</u> _____

Complete each sentence with a different exaggeration from the one in the paragraph.

6. Ellen was so nervous that _____

7. The audience clapped so hard that _____

_____.

B. On separate paper, write four sentences that each contain figurative language.

© Silver, Burdett & Ginn Inc.

Vocabulary: Story Critical Words

A. Study the meaning of each word.

amazed astonished	**moist** slightly wet
bare not covered	**sheltered** gave protection to; gave cover to
gushed flowed out with force	**softening** becoming softer and softer
ledge a narrow shelf of rock	**wept** cried

B. Finish each sentence with the correct vocabulary word.

1. The water _____ from the firefighter's hose.

2. It's better to wear a hat than to go out in the sun with a _____ head.

3. My little brother _____ when his favorite toy broke.

4. Vanessa was _____ at the size of the dinosaur in the museum.

5. It didn't matter that it was windy, because our tent was _____ by the large rock.

6. The mountain climber rested on the _____ and enjoyed the view.

7. The stick of butter was _____ quickly in the warm kitchen.

8. The grass was still _____ with dew when we woke up at camp.

C. Each word is a synonym or an antonym for a vocabulary word. Write the vocabulary word. Then write **S** if it is a synonym or **A** if it is an antonym.

9. hardening _____   12. trickled _____

10. dry _____   13. surprised _____

11. sobbed _____   14. naked _____

D. Write the vocabulary word that could describe each of these things.

15. The ground after a brief rain shower _____

16. A mountain with no trees or shrubs _____

17. The look on your face after seeing a shooting star _____

18. What happens to clay after it has been kneaded _____

19. What your tent did on your camping vacation _____

Vocabulary: Support Words

A. Study the meaning of each word.

chilled made or became cool or cold   **slopes** land that slants up or down
distant far away   **sorrow** sadness
grasp a firm grip or hold of the hand   **sprouted** grew
nestled settled down comfortably   **surge** a sudden, strong rush

B. Sometimes the meaning of a word is given in a clue. Read each sentence clue. Then write the correct vocabulary word.

1. The seeds did this after they were planted and watered. _____

2. When these are covered with snow, you can go sledding down them.

   _____

3. This is what China is from the United States. _____

4. When they go into a big store, Pam will do this to her little sister's hand to keep

   her close. _____

5. When Ramon wanted to make the juice colder, this is what he did to it.

   _____

6. You might feel this if you found out your best friend was moving to another

   town. _____

7. This is what Mr. Brown's pet hamster did in the straw before going to sleep.

   _____

8. If you eat a good breakfast, your energy level might do this. _____

C. Complete each analogy with the correct vocabulary word.

9. *Warmed* is to *heated* as *cooled* is to _____.

10. *Near* is to *close* as *far* is to _____.

11. *Happiness* is to *joy* as *unhappiness* is to _____.

12. *Flat* is to *plains* as *steep* is to _____.

13. *Paw* is to *scratch* as *hand* is to _____.

Figurative Language

Writers use **figurative language** to create a vivid picture in a reader's mind. Notice the underlined words in the examples.

Examples: Those swans glide like white ships on the pond. (simile)

The crowd was a chorus of noisy geese. (metaphor)

Hank thought the spelling quiz was a piece of cake. (idiom)

The racers ran quicker than lightning. (exaggeration)

A. Write the two things that are compared in each sentence.

1. The basketball looked like a giant orange.

_____

2. The gym at Smithtown High School was a battlefield.

_____

3. The cheerleaders were as active and quick as circus acrobats.

_____

B. Write the meaning of the underlined words in each sentence.

4. Betsy and Lisa really hit it off when they met yesterday.

_____

5. Mr. Warren had to pull strings to get seats in the front row.

_____

6. The coach told the skater to give it her best shot.

_____

C. Write the characteristic that is exaggerated in each sentence.

7. My brother seems too lazy to raise even an eyebrow.

_____

8. Jill has a brain that could beat a computer.

_____

Charts

A **chart** or a **table** presents information in columns and rows. A **schedule** is a chart that gives the times that events take place.

Read the schedule. Then answer the questions.

Early Fall Schedule **Fieldstone Falcons Soccer Team** **Fieldstone Junior High School**		
Team	*Date	Place
Hawks	Monday, September 23	home
Lions	Wednesday, September 25	Lawton School
Jets	Tuesday, October 1	home
Comets	Thursday, October 3	home
Hawks	Saturday, October 5	Laredo School
Blues	Monday, October 7	Blue Mills School
*All games will start at 3:30 P.M.		

1. What team is this schedule for? _____

2. When do the Fieldstone Falcons play the Blues? _____

3. Where do the Falcons play the Lions? _____

4. When is the Falcons-Jets soccer game played? _____

5. What team do the Falcons play on Wednesday, September 25? _____

6. How many home games are scheduled for early fall? _____

7. What team do the Falcons play on Thursday, October 3? _____

8. What team do the Falcons play twice? _____

9. What team comes to Fieldstone Junior High on Tuesday, October 1? _____

10. Where is the only weekend game held? _____

11. What team do the Falcons play on Monday, October 7? _____

12. How many ''away'' games are there? _____

13. At what time are the games played? _____

Card Catalog

A **card catalog** or a **computer catalog** lists all the books in a library in alphabetical order. **Title cards** are arranged in a catalog alphabetically by the first main word of the title. **Author cards** are listed alphabetically by the author's last name. Nonfiction books are also listed alphabetically on **subject cards.** The **call number** in the top corner of the card tells you where to find the book on a library shelf.

```
551.46     OCEAN
           Rosen, Kelly N.
               A day under the ocean.
           New York, Sea Life Press, 1988.
           72 p. illus.
```

A. Use the card from a card catalog to answer the questions.

   1. Is this a title card, an author card, or a subject card? _____

   2. What is the title of the book? _____

   3. Who is the author of the book? _____

   4. When was the book published? _____

   5. Is this book fiction or nonfiction? _____

   6. What is the call number of the book? _____

   7. What does this book probably tell you about? _____

B. Write the word or words you would look under in the card catalog to find the following items.

   8. the author of *A History of Soccer* _____

   9. another book by Kelly N. Rosen _____

   10. a book about our solar system _____

   11. a book written by Tony Parish _____

   12. another book about exploring the ocean _____

Prefixes *in-, pre-, re-*

A **prefix** is a word part added to the beginning of a word. It changes the meaning of the word. Read the meanings of the prefixes *in-, re-,* and *pre-.*

in- "not" or "in"   *inability,* "not having the ability"
re- "again" or "back"   *relearn,* "learn again"
pre- "earlier" or "before" *prearrange,* "arrange earlier"

A. Complete each sentence by adding *in-, re-,* or *pre-* to the underlined word. Use the meaning clues to help you choose the correct prefix.

1. Allen wrote to his pen pal, Josef, to _____ Josef's visit.
   (<u>plan</u> earlier)

2. Josef would be picked up at the airport by Allen and his parents.

   Then they would _____ to Allen's house.
   (<u>turn</u> back, or go back)

3. Allen would double check the number of Josef's _____ flight
   ahead of time.   (<u>coming</u> in)

4. Allen suggested that Josef _____ the information he had sent to him
   about New York City.   (<u>read</u> again)

5. If Josef would like to see a play, Allen's parents could get some

   _____ tickets for it.
   (<u>paid</u> for earlier)

6. Allen told Josef that he would be very busy, and never _____,
   once he arrived!   (not <u>active</u>)

B. Now choose from these words. On separate paper, write eight sentences using your choices.

inactive	ingrown	precaution	prepay	rename
incorrect	inland	precondition	rejoin	remodel
indoor	prearrange	prehistoric	reline	replace

Predicting Outcomes

When you read a story and guess what will happen next, or at the end, you are making a **prediction.** A prediction should make sense with the story. Look for clues in the story that give you hints about what will happen next. Use the clues, together with what you know about events like the ones in the story, to predict what will happen.

Story Clues
+ Experience Clues
Prediction

A. Read the story. Write predictions about what will happen next. Then tell why the predictions make sense in the story.

    Carmen and Elisa had been friends since the second grade. They lived right next door to each other. In fact, Carmen's bedroom window was directly across from Elisa's. On this hot August night, Carmen couldn't fall asleep. She sat up in bed and reached for the walkie-talkie that she and Elisa used for talking between their rooms.

1. Prediction: _____

_____

This prediction makes sense because _____

_____

    After climbing out of bed, Carmen signaled Elisa on the walkie-talkie. Elisa answered in a sleepy voice. Carmen talked about all the fun they had that day. Elisa mumbled a few words. Then Carmen suggested that they make plans for what they could do the next day.

2. Prediction: _____

_____

This prediction makes sense in the story because _____

_____

    Elisa said she'd rather make plans in the morning, so Carmen said OK. But when she got back into bed, she began to think about the next day's plans.

B. On separate paper, write the experience clues that helped you make each prediction.

© Silver, Burdett & Ginn Inc.

Vocabulary: Story Critical Words

A. Study the meaning of each word.

correctly   in the correct way; without mistakes
fatal   causing ruin, disaster, or death
fates   outcomes; the way things turn out in the end

forbidden   not allowed
furious   full of anger
incorrectly   not correctly; not properly
permissible   allowable

B. Write the vocabulary word that is a synonym for each word.

1. deadly _____

2. wrongly _____

3. prohibited _____

4. angry _____

5. properly _____

6. disastrous _____

C. Answer the question.

7. What two pairs of vocabulary words are antonyms?

_____   _____

_____   _____

D. Finish each sentence with the correct vocabulary word.

8. The winner of the spelling bee spelled every word _____.

9. Stacy wanted to read the book soon to find out the _____ of the main characters.

10. The club rule said it was _____ to invite guests as long as you asked for permission first.

11. Because he did the addition problem _____, he got the wrong sum.

12. The road crew put salt on the icy roads so drivers would not have _____ accidents.

13. Bo did not go into the lake because people are _____ to swim when there is no lifeguard on duty.

Vocabulary: Support Words

A. Study the meaning of each word.

alphabetical   arranged in the order of the
alphabet

awaits   waits for

committed   did something bad or wrong

national   regarding a nation or country

providing   on the condition that; if

recite   to say aloud before a group of people

tolerated   put up with

B. Finish each sentence with the correct vocabulary word.

1. The ball game would start at 10 A.M., _____ it didn't rain.

2. The president held a news conference to discuss _____ issues.

3. The man _____ a crime when he robbed a bank.

4. Elizabeth had to _____ a poem to her classmates.

5. The card catalog in the library lists titles, authors, and subjects in

    _____ order.

6. The traveler _____ the train's arrival.

7. Jack sometimes _____ his friend's practical jokes.

C. Write the vocabulary word that rhymes with each word.

8. weights _____

9. sight _____

D. Finish each phrase with the vocabulary word that makes the most sense. Write a sentence for each phrase. The first one has been done for you.

10. _alphabetical_ **order:** Words in a dictionary are arranged

    in alphabetical order.

11. _____ **a poem:** _____

    _____

12. _____ **a crime:** _____

    _____

13. _____ **a bus:** _____

    _____

Dictionary

A **dictionary** is made up of entries arranged in alphabetical order that tell how to say the word and what the word means. The two **guide words** at the top of every dictionary page help you find a word quickly. The first guide word is the first entry word on that page. The second guide word is the last entry word on that page.

Read the sample dictionary page.

---

sketch/skim

sketch (skech) *n.* **1.** a simple, rough drawing. **2.** a short outline. **3.** a short scene in a show. *verb* to make a drawing of.

sketchy (skech′ē) *adj.* like a sketch; not complete [a *sketchy* report]. — **sketchier, sketchiest**

ski (skē) *n.* one of a pair of wooden runners used to slide on snow. *verb* to glide on skis. —**skied** (skēd), **skiing** —**skier, noun**

skiff (skif) *n.* a small, light rowboat with a sail.

skill (skil) *n.* **1.** an ability to do something well. **2.** a craft, science, or art that uses the hands or body.

skim (skim) *v.* **1.** to take floating matter from the top of a liquid. **2.** to look at quickly. **3.** to glide lightly over. —**skimmed, skimming**

PRONUNCIATION KEY

a	fat	ī	bite, fire	ou	out	zh	leisure
ā	ape	o	cob	u	up	ŋ	ring
ä	car, lot	o	hop	ur	fur		a *in* ago
e	ten	ō	go	ch	chin		e *in* agent
er	care	ô	law, horn	sh	she	ə =	i *in* unity
ē	even	oi	oil	th	thin		o *in* collect
i	hit	oo	look	*th*	then		u *in* focus
ir	here	ōo	tool				

A. Circle the words that could appear as entry words on this dictionary page.

1. skate   **2.** skillful   **3.** sizzle   **4.** skid   **5.** skip   **6.** skillet

B. Write the correct meaning of each underlined entry word.

7. The actors put on a funny <u>sketch</u> for the audience. _____

8. The sea gull <u>skimmed</u> over the bay. _____

9. The woman <u>skimmed</u> through the paper. _____

C. Write the entry word that you would use to look up each word.

10. skier _____   **11.** skimming _____   **12.** sketchiest _____

Predicting Outcomes

When you read a story and guess what will happen next, you are making a **prediction.** To make predictions that make sense with the story, look for clues in the story and think about what you already know.

Story Clues
+	Experience Clues
Prediction

Answer the questions to tell what you already know about dogs. Then read the story about a dog named Fellow. Use clues in the story and what you already know about dogs to predict what will happen next.

1. What do you know about a dog's senses? _____

_____

2. Why might a dog bark? _____

_____

3. How do dogs usually behave with their owners? _____

_____

Fellow was lying down on the back porch. Chris, his owner, was sitting on the steps reading a magazine. Suddenly, Fellow leaped up, ran down the steps, and stopped in front of the shrubs growing next to the house. Fellow sniffed and wagged his tail. Then he barked as he looked over at Chris.

Predict what you think Chris will do next. _____

_____

Chris went over to the shrubs to see what Fellow was barking about. He parted two branches. There on the ground was a baby rabbit, somehow separated from its mother. Chris patted Fellow and told him to sit.

Predict what you think Fellow will do next. _____

_____

Chris loves animals, and he gently picked up the baby rabbit. Then he tried to think of how to find its mother.

B. On separate paper, write why each of your predictions makes sense.

Prefixes *in-*, *pre-*, *re-*

A **prefix** is a word part added to the beginning of a word. It changes the meaning of the word. Read the meanings of the prefixes *in-*, *re-*, and *pre-*.

in- ''not'' or ''in''   *indirect,* ''not direct''
re- ''again'' or ''back''   *reuse,* ''use again''
pre- ''earlier'' or ''before'' *precut,* ''cut earlier''

A. Complete each pair of sentences by adding *in-*, *re-*, or *pre-* to the underlined word in each sentence. Use context clues in the sentences and the meanings of the prefixes to help you.

1. Richard <u>heated</u> the oven before he started mixing the cake batter.

He _____ the oven.

2. He wanted to <u>pay</u> his sister back by baking her a birthday cake.

He wanted to _____ Robin for helping him yesterday.

3. Richard <u>opened</u> the cookbook again to read what should go into the cake.

He _____ it to the right page.

4. Richard was not an <u>experienced</u> cook.

He was very _____ at baking cakes.

5. He <u>filled</u> the measuring cup again and poured the flour into the bowl.

As he _____ the cup, the flour spilled.

6. Now he wished he had a mix that was <u>packaged</u> earlier.

A _____ mix might be a lot easier!

B. Read the words in the box. On separate paper, write a story using as many of these words as possible.

inattention	inexact	prejudge	rediscover	refuel
indefinite	preheat	preoccupy	refill	rename

© Silver, Burdett & Ginn Inc.

Alphabetical Order

Some lists are in **alphabetical order.** The words are listed from *A* to *Z*. Knowing this order will help you find words in lists. These names are in alphabetical order: Ben, Betsy, Carlos, Cassie, Dana, David, Eliot, Elizabeth.

The words in each of the following lists are in alphabetical order by the first letter. If the second letters are the same, look to the third letter, and so on. Mark an X where you would add each new word to be in alphabetical order in the list.

1. Scott
   Sharon
   Steve
   Where would you put **Sandra**?

2. sauce
   scale
   serve
   Where would you put **season**?

3. tower
   tube
   twice
   Where would you put **trade**?

4. eager
   earn
   earthquake
   Where would you put **easily**?

5. honk
   hood
   hotel
   Where would you put **horrible**?

6. bait
   banana
   bargain
   battle
   Where would you put **baggage**?

7. alarm
   alert
   altogether
   Where would you put **alive**?

8. what
   which
   who
   Where would you put **when**?

9. Marcy
   Marita
   Mark
   Where would you put **Marty**?

10. canary
    candle
    canyon
    Where would you put **cannon**?

11. flag
    flame
    flare
    Where would you put **flat**?

12. groan
    groom
    grow
    growl
    Where would you put **grocery**?

Figurative Language

Similes, metaphors, idioms, and exaggeration are different types of **figurative language**.

> Examples: The <u>sun</u> looks <u>like a golden coin</u>. (simile)
> The <u>traffic jam was a sea of metal</u>. (metaphor)
> My solution really <u>hit the nail on the head</u>. (idiom)
> The cat was so startled that it <u>jumped a mile</u>. (exaggeration)

A. Use each phrase in a sentence that compares two different things.

1. as quiet as

_____

2. as sharp as

_____

3. stormy ocean was

_____

4. noisy children are

_____

B. Write a sentence that shows the meaning of each idiom.

5. turn over a new leaf _____

_____

6. keep a straight face _____

_____

7. spill the beans _____

_____

C. Complete each sentence with an exaggeration.

8. It was so cold that _____

9. The air was filled with _____

Following Directions

Directions tell you how to do something. Read or listen to directions carefully.

Pretend that you have just moved to Greenfield. The directions will help you do your Saturday errands. Start at the X at your apartment building at 555 Causeway Avenue. Draw a line to show where you would go as you follow each direction.

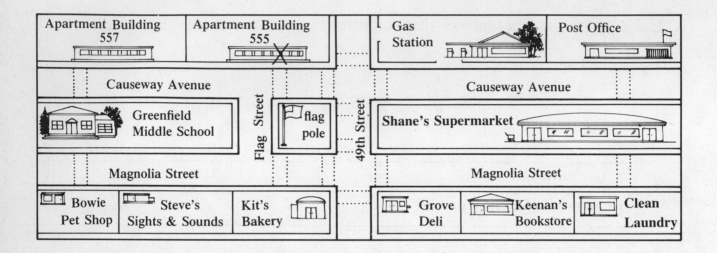

1. In front of your building, cross the street. Walk down Flag Street, past the flagpole on your left. Cross Magnolia Street.

2. Turn right on Magnolia Street. Go to Steve's Sights & Sounds, where you can buy the record you want. It is the first store on your left after Kit's Bakery.

3. Leaving Steve's, turn right and head back down Magnolia Street to the corner of 49th Street. Cross 49th Street and walk straight ahead, past the Grove Deli. Keenan's Bookstore, where you want to get a paperback for your dad, is the second store on the right.

4. To go to the supermarket for the bread and milk, turn left outside Keenan's Bookstore. Go back down Magnolia Street to the corner of 49th Street. Turn right and cross Magnolia Street. Shane's Supermarket is the first building on your right.

5. To get to the post office, turn right outside the supermarket entrance. Turn right again at the corner of Causeway Avenue. Walk half a block, and cross the street. The post office is right there.

6. To get back home, turn right outside the post office and head west on Causeway. Cross 49th Street, and you'll be back to your apartment building.

Vocabulary: Story Critical Words

A. Study the meaning of each word.

complicated   hard to solve or understand
consonants   any letters in the alphabet except *a, e, i, o, u*, and *y*
reversed   moved backwards

syllable   a word or a part of a word spoken with a single sound
translating   putting into words of a different language

B. One word in each sentence does not make sense. Circle that word. Then write the vocabulary word that should go there.

1. Because she had studied hard for it, Anne thought her math test was not

   completed. _____

2. The professor was an expert at tracing English into French. _____

3. Debbie could not remember how to spell the first silly of the word *psychiatrist*.

   _____

4. Leslye rehearsed the car into the garage. _____

C. Complete each analogy with the correct vocabulary word.

5. *Simple* is to *easy* as *hard* is to _____ .

6. *The letters* a *and* u *are to* vowels *as the letters* j *and* t *are*

   to _____ .

7. *Chain* is to *link* as *word* is to _____ .

D. Finish each phrase with the vocabulary word that makes the most sense. Write a sentence for each phrase. The first one has been done for you.

8. reversed _____ the car: Dr. Bell reversed the car to
   _____
   get out of the parking space _____ .

9. _____ the Spanish words: _____

   _____

10. A _____ task: _____

    _____

Vocabulary: Support Words

A. Study the meaning of each word.

coyote   a small wolf
eavesdropping   listening to a private
conversation

Pig Latin   an invented language
rundown   in bad condition; falling apart
southwestern   in, of, or from the southwest

B. Write the correct vocabulary word for each clue.

1. To talk in a secret language, you might talk in this. _____

2. A spy might be doing this to find out secrets. _____

3. Belongings, might become this. _____

4. You might see this on a prairie. _____

C. Read each row of words. Write the vocabulary word that belongs to the same group.

5. worn, junky, old, _____

6. northeastern, northwestern, southeastern, _____

7. sneaking, spying, snooping, _____

D. Pig Latin is a secret language. The message below is written in the secret language of
a club. To find out what each word says, circle every other letter, beginning with the
first letter of the word. Then write the letters you have circled. The first word is done.

Ⓜ A Ⓔ A Ⓒ T Ⓥ I Ⓕ N Ⓗ Ⓖ   A E T   T F H D E
C O L I U M B J H T O M U R S V E   T L O C N K I L G J H S T

8. _____ _____ _____ _____ _____

9. Where will the meeting be? _____

10. When will it be? _____

E. Read each row of words. Draw a line under the word that does not belong in the row.
Write the vocabulary word that does belong there.

11. spying, drawing, listening, _____

12. piled, broken, ruined, _____

13. northern, upstairs, westward, _____

Dictionary

A **dictionary** contains alphabetical entries that tell how to pronounce the entry word and what the word means. To find words quickly, use the two **guide words** at the top of each page.

Read the sample dictionary page.

---

cheerful/cherish

cheerful (chir′fəl) *adj.* **1.** glad. **2.** bright and joyful. **3.** willing to help. —**cheerfully, cheerfulness**

cheerleader (chir′lē′dər) *n.* a person who leads others to cheer.

PRONUNCIATION KEY

a	fat	ī	bite, fire	ou	out	zh leisure
ā	ape	o	cob	u	up	nĝ ring
ä	car, lot	o	hop	ur	fur	a *in* ago
e	ten	ō	go	ch	chin	e *in* agent
er	care	ô	law, horn	sh	she	ə = i *in* unity
ē	even	oi	oil	th	thin	o *in* collect
i	hit	๐๐	look	*th*	then	u *in* focus
ir	here	ōō	tool			

cheerless (chir′lis) *adj.* sad; not cheerful. —**cheerlessly**

cheese (chēz) *n.* a food made from soured milk.

chef (shef) *n.* **1.** the head cook in a restaurant. **2.** any cook.

chemist (kem′ist) *n.* an expert in chemistry.

cherish (cher′ish) *v.* **1.** to treat with great care. **2.** to keep a feeling or idea strongly in mind.

A. Draw a line through the words that would *not* appear on this dictionary page.

1. chestnut **3.** cheesecloth **5.** chair **7.** cheery **9.** chemistry
2. cheetah **4.** checkerboard **6.** chew **8.** chess **10.** chemical

B. Circle the number of the meaning for the underlined word in each sentence.

11. Don's <u>cheerful</u> helper even works on Saturdays.   1   2   3

12. What memory of that trip do you <u>cherish</u> the most?   1   2

13. Ms. Dale is the <u>chef</u> at the Rainbow Grill.   1   2

C. Write the entry word that you would use to look up each word in the list.

14. cheerfulness _____

15. cheerlessly _____

© Silver, Burdett & Ginn Inc.

Choosing Among Resources

The library has many kinds of **resources,** or reference sources.

> **card catalog**—lists books in the library in alphabetical order by title, author's last name, and also by subject if the book is nonfiction
> **dictionary**—gives the pronunciation and meanings of each word
> **encyclopedia**—contains articles about different topics arranged alphabetically
> **newspaper**—gives current information about local, national, and world events
> **telephone directory**—in yellow pages, lists businesses and services alphabetically within categories

A. Read the sentences. Write which reference source will give the necessary information.

1. Luisa went to the library. She needed information about the first telephones. First she looked under *telephone* in the _____ .

2. When she read about Alexander Graham Bell's invention, she came across the unfamiliar word *transmitted*. She looked up this word in the _____ .

3. Next, Luisa wanted the call number for the book *Inventions That Changed the World*. She looked for the title in the _____ .

4. Luisa also wanted facts about today's telephones. To find out what nearby stores sell telephone answering machines, she used the _____ .

5. Finally, she read about a local citizen who reported an accident and saved lives by using a car phone. She found the story in the _____ .

B. Underline the reference you would use to answer each question.

6. When did Marie Curie discover radium?

    dictionary   encyclopedia

7. What is a puffin?

    card catalog   dictionary

8. Who wrote *Save the Wilderness*?

    card catalog   newspaper

9. What stores sell snorkels and fins?

    newspaper   telephone directory

Test-Taking

The purpose of a **test** is to check your understanding of a certain subject. There are four basic kinds of tests: **true-false, matching, completion,** and **multiple choice.** Of the four, multiple choice is the most common and can include the other three.

> ### Guidelines for Test-Taking
> ◆ Read the statements carefully.
> ◆ Follow the directions exactly when you answer.
> ◆ Answer things you are sure of first.
> ◆ Check your answers.

1. Fill in the circle beside the word that best completes the sentence.

   Dinosaurs and dodo birds were once common, but now they are _____.

   ○ native   ○ enthusiastic
   ○ bothersome   ○ extinct

2. Circle the letter before the correct answer.

   The three words below belong to which category?

   animals   people   plants
      a. domestic animals   c. nonliving things
      b. living things   d. things people love

3. Read the statement. Then read the sentences that follow it. Circle **T** for **true.** Circle **F** for **false.**

   Orchids grow well in the hot and damp weather of tropical countries.
   Blossoms of the yucca plant do best in countries where the weather is cold and dry.

   T   F   Orchids like hot, damp weather.

   T   F   Yucca blossoms like cold and wet weather.

4. Circle the letter before the meaning that matches that of the underlined word.

   Some dinosaurs were <u>enormous</u> animals.

      a. average   c. huge
      b. entertaining   d. miniscule

Main Idea/Details

The **main idea** tells what a paragraph is about. Sometimes the main idea is stated in a sentence in the paragraph. When the main idea is not stated directly, the reader must decide on the main idea by thinking about what idea the details tell about. **Supporting details** are words, phrases, or sentences that go with the main idea. A detail that does not support the main idea is a **nonsupporting detail.**

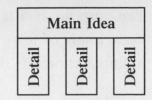

A. Read each paragraph. Underline the stated main idea sentence. Then, from the details below each paragraph, circle one that would support the main idea. Cross out the nonsupporting details.

1. Animals have many kinds of coverings. Bears, wolves, rabbits, and lions are covered with fur. Elephants have thick, tough skin. Armadillos are covered with bony plates, or ''armor.''

   Armadillos burrow into the ground.
   The turtle's special covering is its shell.
   Armadillos have short legs.

2. *Bank* can mean ''a place for keeping money'' or ''a large mound of earth.'' *Trunk* can mean ''the main stem of a tree'' or ''a large box for storing things.'' *Soil* can mean ''the top layer of earth,'' or ''to make or become dirty.'' *Swallow* can mean ''to let food or drink go through the throat into the stomach,'' or ''a small, swift-flying bird.'' Many words have more than one meaning.

   Soil can mean ''the top layer of earth'' or ''to make or become dirty.''
   Run can mean ''move rapidly.''
   Some words have only one meaning.

B. Read the paragraph. Circle the letter of the sentence that tells the main idea.

3. The wind can lift seeds from trees, bushes, and flowers and scatter them far and near. Birds, insects, and animals often carry seeds from one place to another on their bodies. Seeds also can be carried by rainwater. Even ocean waters can carry seeds from one shore to another.

   a. Seeds fly. **b.** These are ways seeds get scattered.

   c. Plants and animals help each other.

Drawing Conclusions

Drawing conclusions means putting the information an author gives you in a story with what you already know. A **conclusion** is a summary statement you can make after reading a story or part of the story.

Story Clues
Experience Clues
Conclusion

+

Read the example. Notice that the conclusion can be drawn from the underlined story clues along with what you know from your own experience.

Example: The grapevine was <u>almost bare</u>. Old Fred Fox's <u>stomach was now full</u>.
A grin formed on his <u>purple-smeared</u> mouth. <u>"Yum, yum!"</u> said Old Fred.

Conclusion: <u>Old Fred Fox was hungry and had just eaten lots of grapes.</u>
Experience: <u>A full stomach comes from eating a lot. Grapes are juicy and taste good. Some grapes are purple.</u>

A. Read the passage. Select the conclusion that makes sense, and then write it. Underline the clues in the story that lead you to the conclusion. Then write what you know that also supports the conclusion.

Lan looked out the window. She ran to the closet and found her warm jacket with the hood. Then she pulled on her boots and grabbed her mittens. Outside everything looked so white! "Yippee!" Lan cried as she romped in the soft drifts that covered the ground.

1. Conclusion: _____

_____

There was a sale on winter clothing, so Lan got a new jacket.
It is winter, and Lan is happy about the new snow.
It is a cold winter night, and snow is falling.

2. Experience: _____

_____

B. Read the passage. On separate paper, write a conclusion based on story clues and your own experience.

3. Gina was fixing Joe's bike in the garage. Over in a corner was the vacuum cleaner Mom had asked her to repair. Up in her room, Gina had Ron's kite to fix. Gina was hurrying with the bike because she had to get to her other fix-it jobs.

Vocabulary: Story Critical Words

A. Study the meaning of each word.

accuse   blame
hesitated   stopped because of doubt
historian   an expert in history
identical   exactly alike
innocent   not guilty

secret service   a government office that does special detective work
theory   an explanation of why something happens
undercover   acting or done in secret

B. Complete each analogy with the correct vocabulary word.

1. *Science* is to *scientist* as *history* is to _____.

2. *Wrong* is to *right* as *guilty* is to _____.

3. *Unlike* is to *different* as *same* is to _____.

4. *Halted* is to *stopped* as *paused* is to _____.

C. Write the correct vocabulary word for each clue.

5. Members of this group provide security for the president. _____

6. A scientist might do many experiments to prove this. _____

7. A police officer wearing a disguise on the job is this. _____

8. This is what twins often are. _____

9. This person could tell you about things that happened

   in the past. _____

10. Someone who didn't know how to answer a question might have done this before

    speaking. _____

D. Write the vocabulary word that is a synonym for each of these words.

11. same _____

12. paused _____

13. charge _____

14. blameless _____

15. find fault with _____

16. idea _____

17. secretly _____

18. guiltless _____

19. opinion _____

20. felt unwilling _____

Vocabulary: Support Words

A. Study the meaning of each word.

aground   on or onto the ground
articles   pieces of writing on a single subject
denies   says that something is not true
initial   the first letter of a name
intrigue   a secret or sneaky plot

pamphlet   a thin book with a paper cover
publishing   preparing a book, magazine, or newspaper for sale
pursuit   the act of following or trying to catch up to

B. Read each row of words. Write the vocabulary word that belongs to the same group.

1. magazine, newspaper, book, _____

2. writing, proofreading, editing, _____

3. stories, columns, reviews, _____

C. Answer each question with the correct vocabulary word.

4. What starts your name and rhymes with *official*? _____

5. What will you be when your boat touches the beach? _____

6. What might you write if you worked for a newspaper? _____

7. Which word has eyes but can't see? _____

8. What is a company that produces magazines doing? _____

9. What kind of story makes you wonder? _____

10. What kind of activity are you in if you chase your cat? _____

D. Finish each phrase with the vocabulary word that makes the most sense. Write a sentence for each phrase. The first one has been done for you.

11. newspaper ___articles___ : We read several newspaper articles
    about the election for mayor. _____

12. in _____ of the thief: _____
    _____

13. _____ the report: _____
    _____

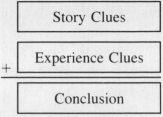

Drawing Conclusions

A **conclusion** is a summary statement you can make after reading a story or part of the story. **Conclusions** are not always stated in the story. To **draw conclusions,** you must think about the information given in the story and what you already know.

Story Clues
Experience Clues
Conclusion

A. Read each story. Circle the letter of the conclusion that goes best with the information in the story. Then write what you know that helped you to choose that conclusion.

1. José sat down on the bench. He put his fingers on the keys. Then José began to play the new song he was learning.

   a. José has a new piano.   **b.** José was practicing his piano lesson.

   c. José is clever.

   Experience: _____

   _____

   _____

2. After stepping up to the plate, Erica wound up to swing. The ball flew toward her. Erica swung hard and hit the ball.

   a. Erica's team won the game.   **b.** Erica is good at sports.

   c. Erica plays on a softball team.

   Experience: _____

   _____

   _____

3. Henry was walking home from school. It started to snow very hard. Soon the snow covered Henry's shoes. Then the snow was up to Henry's ankles.

   a. Henry should take a bus.   **b.** Henry needs new shoes.   **c.** Henry walks fast.

   Experience: _____

   _____

   _____

B. Underline the words in the stories that helped you draw the conclusions.

Summarizing

When you **summarize** a story, you tell about the story very briefly in your own words. One way to summarize a story is tell the main character's problem and how it was solved.

A. Read the story about Karisia. Then write notes after the story.

It was 2433, and Karisia had been on the planetary exploration mission with her parents for well over a year now. She had plenty to do with chores and school work, but she wanted to do more.

Karisia had read in history about people leaving messages inside containers. That's what she wanted to do. She wanted to leave messages for others who might visit some of the same places she had visited.

The problem was that most of the places the ship visited had no inhabitants—no one lived there. Therefore, there were no message centers. The planet Karisia's family explored now was uninhabited, but it was beautiful. The soil was a sparkling green. The rocks also sparkled in colors of pink, blue, and gold. Then it came to her! Karisia decided that she would leave a huge message for all those coming or going to see.

She set about gathering sparkling rocks and spelled them out in this pattern. *Karisia, 9 years old, from Earth, here in 2433*. Then Karisia stood back and smiled.

1. Where/When _____

2. Who _____

3. Problem _____

4. Event _____

5. Outcome _____

B. Write a brief summary of the story in your own words. Use your notes to help you.

_____

_____

_____

C. On separate paper, write a brief summary of a favorite story or TV show that is fresh in your mind. Tell about only the most important ideas. Tell the main character's problem and how it was solved.

Cause/Effect

An **effect** is what happens. A **cause** is what makes it happen. Writers sometimes use words and phrases like *because, if, so, since, as a result,* and *therefore* to signal causes and effects.

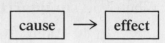

cause → effect

Read the paragraphs about the pony express. Answer the questions. Then circle the signal words in the paragraphs.

In the early 1860s, there was no railroad line running from Missouri to California. Therefore, it was hard to get mail from the east to people in California. In April of 1860, the pony express was started. Under the pony express system, horseback riders carried mail from Missouri to California. It was a long, hard ride. Both horses and riders needed places to rest, so pony express stations were built along the route.

The pony express riders almost never lost the mail. Because the pony express system worked well, more riders, horses, and stations were added. It was only when a railroad line was built to California that the pony express system ended.

1. Why was it hard to get mail to California in the early 1860s?

_____

_____

2. Why were pony express stations built along the routes?

_____

_____

3. What happened as a result of the pony express system working well?

_____

_____

4. What caused the pony express to end?

_____

_____

B. On separate paper, write a sentence of your own that tells about a cause and an effect.

Classification

Words can be **classified,** or grouped together, according to ways that they are alike. The whole group of words is often called a category or a class.

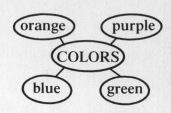

Read each row of words. Cross out the word that does not belong. Then underline the class to which the words belong or are related in some way. The first one is done for you.

1. ~~groceries~~   envelopes   stamps   letters   mailboxes
   a. supermarket   b. hardware store   c. <u>mail</u>

2. bat   ball   base   hockey stick   mitt
   a. indoor games   b. baseball   c. ice hockey

3. jolly   merry   glad   cheerful   cautious
   a. happy   b. sad   c. angry

4. slide   run   jump   leap   sad
   a. feelings   b. actions   c. sports

5. article   headline   index   library   news
   a. television   b. newspaper   c. bulletin board

6. end   finish   complete   start   stop
   a. ways of beginning   b. opposite meaning   c. similar meaning

7. buzz   jingle   clang   hum   fuzzy
   a. sounds   b. sights   c. movements

8. trees   sun   stars   moon   clouds
   a. ocean   b. land   c. sky

9. coyote   bobcat   raccoon   dog   beaver
   a. farm animals   b. wild animals   c. pets

Characterization

Character **traits** are special qualities of personality. They can be seen in the speech, actions, and thoughts of a character. **Emotions** are what a character's feelings are at a certain time. Traits do not usually change in a story, but feelings may change.

Read the story. Then choose the best answer to each question and write it.

This week the Mirror Writing Club was holding its weekly meeting at the home of the club's new president.

"Where's a pen?" asked Judy. "I left mine somewhere." Judy was never ready to begin a meeting on time. "What should we discuss first?"

"We agreed last time that the club should vote on a new member," Ivan reminded Judy.

"That's right!" Judy exclaimed. "Let's take a vote."

Everyone agreed that Kerry should become a member of the club. Judy smiled when the final vote was counted. Kerry was a new classmate, and Judy liked her.

Then Judy interrupted the meeting to telephone Kerry. "Kerry, welcome to the Mirror Writing Club! I hope to see you at next week's meeting," said Judy.

Then, as the group continued their meeting, Ivan argued to limit the club to seven people. Judy frowned when the other four members agreed with Ivan.

1. How would you describe Judy? _____

   fussy   shy   thoughtful   disorganized   patient

2. How does the writer show you what Judy is like? _____

   _____

   Judy welcomed Kerry to the club.
   Judy smiled brightly after the vote.
   Judy said that she left her pen somewhere.

3. How did Judy feel when Kerry was voted into the club? _____

   disappointed   amused   upset   angry   happy

4. Why do you think Judy frowned? _____

   _____

   She felt sad that the meeting would be over soon.
   She disagreed with the rest of the members of the club.
   She did not like hearing Ivan argue.

Vocabulary: Story Critical Words

A. Study the meaning of each word.

admit   to accept as true; confess
astonishment   amazement; great surprise
disturbing   bothering
doubtfully   in an unsure way

notions   small, useful things, such as needles, threads, and scissors
peculiar   odd
tremendous   very large

B. One word in each sentence does not make sense. Underline that word. Then write the vocabulary word that belongs in its place.

1. Everybody was full of embarrassment at the fireworks display.

   _____

2. Sid found some blue thread in the drawer full of potions.   _____

3. It would be very familiar to see a fish with wings.   _____

C. Complete each unfinished sentence with the correct vocabulary word.

4. Have you ever seen an elephant? It is _____ in its size.

5. Pete wasn't sure he knew the answer to Annie's question. He answered

   _____ .

6. Mom asked me if I remembered to put the dishes away. I had to

   _____ that I had forgotten.

7. The carpenters were hammering around the house. The noise they made was

   _____ the neighbors.

8. Dad found the broken vase. I had to _____ that I broke it.

9. To fix his torn shirt, Sam got the box of _____ out of the drawer.

10. As the cat leaped through the window, the baby watched in _____ .

D. Each word below is a synonym or an antonym for a vocabulary word. Write the vocabulary word. Then write **S** if it is a synonym or **A** if it is an antonym.

11. small _____

12. surely _____

13. irritating _____

14. deny _____

Vocabulary: Support Words

A. Study the meaning of each word.

appetite   a desire for food
beetle   an insect that has two pairs of wings
chatting   talking in an easy manner
clatter   a series of clashing sounds
heedlessly   carelessly; without paying
 attention

indignantly   with anger about something
 that seems unfair
muttered   talked in a low voice with the lips
 almost closed
radiant   shining brightly
triumphantly   joyfully, because of a success

B. Finish each incomplete sentence with the correct vocabulary word.

1. Sam lost his keys, and Sue cut her finger. The two friends talked

 _____ about their bad luck.

2. Jeff's mother told him to take his umbrella because it might rain. Jeff acted

 _____ when he left home without it.

3. Christine worked hard in the yard all afternoon. She had a huge

 _____ at dinner.

4. It was a warm summer day. The sun was _____ in the sky.

5. The players on the winning team were proud of their success. They held up their

 trophy _____ .

6. The teacher asked Sam to repeat his question. She hadn't heard it the first time

 because he had _____ it.

7. Grandfather hated bugs in his garden. He was upset when he found a

 _____ on his favorite rosebush.

8. The baby was playing with pots and pans. When she dropped them, there was a

 loud _____ .

C. Answer the question.

9. Which two vocabulary words refer to ways people can talk?

 _____

Reading Rate

The **style** and **rate** of your reading depends on your purpose for reading and on how easy or difficult the material is for you. When you read for new information, you first try to get a general idea of the topic and then read, take notes, and reread the text. When you read for entertainment, you pay attention to the story characters or main idea and enjoy the parts that interest you most. This is called **reading style.** How fast or slow you read is your **reading rate.**

Read the passages. Time your reading of each passage. Then write the phrase that best describes your reading rate and purpose for each.

read more slowly for new information   **read more quickly for entertainment**

1. Tabatha and Jess examined the old, yellowed map. They studied the faded lines. ''Where is this big oak tree and rock?'' asked Jess.

   ''I've seen those,'' answered Tabatha. ''The new supermarket is being built there!''

   Jess and Tabatha hurried to the building site. They found both the tree and the rock that marked the place where the old coins were buried.

   Time: _____ _____

2. The first maps were made more than 6,000 years ago. They were discovered near an ancient city called Babylon. In those days, people drew their maps on clay and then baked the clay until it hardened. These ancient maps showed the boundary lines of property.

   Time: _____ _____

3. Ptolemy was in charge of the huge library in ancient Alexandria. Ptolemy collected many different maps into a large book called an *atlas*. The atlas had a map of the world on the final page. However, the shapes of the *continents* were drawn incorrectly. The distances between places were wrong.

   Time: _____ _____

4. Underline key words and phrases, those that tell the most important ideas.

5. Read each passage again and time yourself. Concentrate on key words and phrases.

6. Write your new time after the description of your reading rate.

Characterization

A character's traits, special qualities of personality, do not change throughout a story. However, depending on what is happening, a character's feelings may change.

Read the story. Complete the character trait map by writing phrases from the story that show each trait. Then answer the questions.

Because of an accident, Trish could not move her arms and legs. Now she was one of the lucky students who would learn to operate a special computer by speaking to it. Trish felt nervous when she saw her new teacher come down the hall toward the computer room. But she really wanted to learn how to use this computer.

When she saw how thick the instruction book was, Trish felt slightly discouraged. There would be so much to learn! Then she listened carefully to Ms. Alexander. She watched every step shown to her. Trish studied the pictures in the book and asked a lot of questions.

Finally, Trish figured out a step all by herself. She felt proud when the computer responded to her voice. "Bravo!" exclaimed Ms. Alexander with a smile. "You've done it, Trish!"

1. determined

3. clever

Trish

2. curious

4. observant

1. How did Trish feel about learning to use a special computer?

_____

2. Why was Trish discouraged? _____

_____

3. What do you think will happen if Ms. Alexander shows Trish a new computer

program? _____

© Silver, Burdett & Ginn Inc.

Drawing Conclusions

To **draw conclusions,** you must think about the information the writer has told you in the story along with what you already know. A **conclusion** is a summary statement you can make after reading the story or part of the story.

| Story Clues |
| Experience Clues |
| Conclusion |

+

Read each story. Write the word or words that best complete the conclusion sentence. Underline the clues in the story that helped you draw the conclusion. Then write what you know that supports the conclusion.

1. Suki watched the parade from Cross Street. Her brother was marching and carrying a flag. After the parade, Suki and her family would have a picnic lunch. That night they would all go to the town park to watch the fireworks.

The town was celebrating _____ .

Thanksgiving Day   Independence Day   Valentine's Day

Experience clues: _____

_____

_____

_____

2. When Lucy came back out to the patio, she frowned and shook her head. Her knitting basket was tipped over. The yarn for the scarf she was knitting was all over the floor. Several small pieces seemed to be missing, too. She was glad to share the yarn and wondered if her aunt had taken some. But Aunt Kate would never leave such a mess! Suddenly Lucy noticed two birds flapping their wings and chattering. They were building their nest in the tree right next to the patio.

The yarn had been _____ .

taken by Aunt Kate   lost by Lucy   taken by the birds

Experience clues: _____

_____

_____

_____

Long Word Decoding

When you read long words, use what you know about word parts and about syllables to figure out how to pronounce the word. Follow these rules:

1. Look for words or word parts you know. (*doorstep*, honest*ly*)
2. Divide what is left into syllables. (hon est)
3. Say each part slowly.
4. Try out different vowel sounds. (bone, on, rest)

Read each long word and its meaning. Finish each sentence by circling the correct answer.

distasteful   (not to one's taste or liking)

1. The prefix in the word is _____.   de   dis   ta

2. The *a* in the second syllable sounds like the *a* in _____.

    all   cast   gate

3. The *u* in the suffix *ful* sounds like the *u* in _____.   awful   run   fuel

4. There are _____ syllables in *distasteful*.   3   4   5

flamboyant   (too showy or fancy)

5. The *a* in the first syllable sounds like the *a* in _____.

    arm   lamp   flame

6. The *a* in the last syllable sounds like the *a* in _____.   annoy   say   yarn

7. The second syllable rhymes with _____.   by   toy   how

8. There are _____ syllables in *flamboyant*.   3   4   5

counterpane   (bedspread)

9. What two shorter words make up this compound word?

    _____   _____

10. The last syllable rhymes with _____.   main   man   mine

11. The *ou* in the first syllable sounds like the *ou* in _____.

    out   four   rough

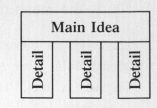
Main Idea/Details

When the **main idea** is stated, a sentence in the paragraph tells the main idea. When the **main idea** is unstated, there is no main idea sentence. Then you must decide what main idea the details in the paragraph tell about. **Supporting details** are sentences that tell about the main idea. A **nonsupporting detail** does not relate to the main idea or to the other details.

Main Idea		
Detail	Detail	Detail

A. Read the paragraph. Choose the sentence that tells the main idea of the paragraph and then write it.

1. Telephone, radio, television, and film are popular ways of getting and giving messages today. Long ago, people made cave writings with pictures to tell about daily life. Some people on Pacific islands tell stories through special dances. People who are deaf often use sign language to give and receive messages.

   Main Idea: _____

   _____

   Dancing is a good way to get messages across.
   People have a lot to say.
   People have used many ways to give and get messages.
   People made cave pictures long ago.

B. Write the details that support the main idea. Draw a line through the nonsupporting detail. **MI** stands for main idea. **SD** stands for supporting detail.

2. MI   Players of these three sports use special equipment.

   SD _____

   SD _____

   SD _____

   Hockey players use skates, sticks, and pucks.
   Some skating rinks are open to the public.
   Skis and poles are used by skiers.
   Scuba divers use flippers and air tanks.

Vocabulary: Story Critical Words

A. Study the meaning of each word.

entirely   including all the parts
identifiable   able to be recognized
legend   a story that is handed down through
   the years that may or may not be partly true

literally   based on the actual words and their
   exact meaning
origin   the place from which something
   comes; beginnings
originally   at the start; at first

B. Choose the vocabulary word that is a synonym for the underlined word in the sentence. Then rewrite the sentence with that word. The first one has been done for you.

1. My cousin's car is <u>recognizable</u> from a long way away because of its bright red stripe.   <u>My cousin's car is identifiable from a long way away because of its</u> <u>bright red stripe.</u>

2. The house painter spread out a drop cloth that covered the couch <u>completely</u>.

_____

_____

3. Many kinds of music have their <u>beginnings</u> in Africa. _____

_____

C. Complete each unfinished sentence with the correct vocabulary word.

4. The phrase "I'm all tied up" _____ means "I am bound with rope."

5. North America was _____ inhabited by Native Americans.

6. The story of King Arthur and the Knights of the Round Table is a famous _____. It takes place in England in the Middle Ages.

7. Some animals, such as skunks and raccoons, have clear markings. This makes them easily _____.

8. The huge quilt covered the bed _____.

9. Many English words have come to us from other languages. For example, the English word *industry* has its _____ in the Latin word *industria*.

Vocabulary: Support Words

A. Study the meaning of each word.

clumsy   awkward; not having good control over one's movements

compass   an instrument for showing directions north, south, east, and west

fiery   like fire; very hot

imitate   to copy the way something acts or sounds

refer   to speak of

B. Answer each question with the correct vocabulary word.

1. Chili that is made with a lot of red peppers might taste this way.

   _____

2. Explorers relied on this to find their way.   _____

3. A parrot can do this to sounds.   _____

4. A book about cars would not do this to bicycles.   _____

5. The juggler pretended to trip to make people think she was this.

   _____

C. Complete each unfinished sentence with the correct vocabulary word.

6. The firefighters heard the alarm. They rushed to the _____ scene.

7. The sailor knew he would reach land if he sailed directly north.

   He would use his _____ to stay on course.

8. Mindy liked a Charlie Chaplin film she saw. She tried to _____ the

   actor's funny walk for her friends.

9. The clown stumbled all over the stage. He did this to appear _____.

10. The writer will give a speech. It will _____ to her latest book.

D. Read each row of words. Draw a line under the word that does not belong in the row. Write the vocabulary word that does belong there.

11. awkward, surprised, uncontrolled, _____

12. rounded, burning, hot, _____

13. shovel, tool, guide, _____

Dictionary

A **dictionary** is made up of entries arranged in alphabetical order that tell how to say the word and what the word means. The two **guide words** at the top of every dictionary page help you find a word quickly. The first guide word is the first entry word on that page. The second guide word is the last entry word.

Read the sample dictionary page.

---

ladder/landing

ladder (lad′ər) *n.* **1.** two long pieces of wood connected by wooden rungs. **2.** something that helps a person go higher.

PRONUNCIATION KEY

a	fat	ī	bite, fire	ou	out	zh	leisure
ā	ape	o	cob	u	up	nĝ	ring
ä	car, lot	o	hop	ur	fur		a *in* ago
e	ten	ō	go	ch	chin		e *in* agent
er	care	ô	law, horn	sh	she	ə =	i *in* unity
ē	even	oi	oil	th	thin		o *in* collect
i	hit	oo	look	th	then		u *in* focus
ir	here	oo	tool				

lag (lag) *v.* to move very slowly; to fall behind. —**lagged, lagging**

lair (ler) *n.* the bed or resting place of a wild animal.

lamp (lamp) *n.* **1.** a thing for giving light, such as an electric bulb. **2.** such a thing with the stand that it is set in [a table *lamp*].

landing (lan′diñg) *n.* **1.** a coming to shore. **2.** a place where a ship can land. **3.** a place at the end of stairs. **4.** a coming to a stop after jumping or falling.

A. Use the guide words to circle the words that could be entry words on this dictionary page.

1. ladybug **2.** lantern **3.** lap **4.** lamb **5.** lace **6.** land

B. Write the number of the correct meaning of the underlined entry word.

7. The ship slowly made its way to the <u>landing</u>. _____

8. Patty had a hard <u>landing</u> at the end of her high jump. _____

C. Use the dictionary page to answer these questions.

9. Which entry word would you look up to find the meaning of *lagging*? _____

10. Would you fall asleep in a *lair*? Why or why not? _____

_____

Homographs

Homographs are words that are spelled the same but are pronounced differently and have different meanings. *Lead* rhyming with *bed* means "a heavy, soft, gray metal," and *lead* rhyming with *seed* means "to show the way." The words *lead* and *lead* are homographs.

Read the sentences. Write the meaning of each underlined homograph. Use context clues to help you.

air that moves strongly	information in a book
completely happy	to give or offer
a gift	to move forward
improvement or advancement	to turn or coil around something

1. On the day of the kite contest, the <u>wind</u> blew fiercely.

_____

2. I watched my kite string <u>wind</u> around a tree branch.

_____

3. At first I was <u>content</u> to wait until the kite came loose.

_____

4. The <u>contents</u> of my kite book told how to get a kite down easily.

_____

5. I made some <u>progress</u> after working on the kite for a few minutes.

_____

6. Then the contest judges started to <u>progress</u> toward me.

_____

7. One judge held out a prize and said, "I <u>present</u> our funniest kite award to *High Flyer*."

_____

8. "Please accept this <u>present</u> from the judges," she said as she gave me the prize.

_____

Charts

Charts and tables present information in columns and rows. A schedule is a chart that gives the times that events take place. Column and row headings help you locate the information.

TV Views		
Tuesday, April 12		
6:00 P.M.	Channel 55	Local news with Dana Hartman.
	Channel 23	Local news with Sharon Billings.
6:30 P.M.	Channel 68	*Guess That Tune*. Game show.
	Channel 49	*News Around the Nation*.
7:00 P.M.	Channel 71	*Inner Worlds*. New plant forms discovered in a rain forest.
	Channel 82	*Crooked Clues*. Mystery.
	Channel 55	*The Governor's Race*. A debate.

Use the television schedule to answer the questions.

1. What is the title of the schedule? _____

2. Which channel is *Guess That Tune* on? _____

3. Which channels give the local news? _____

4. At what time does *Inner Worlds* come on? _____

5. Why might someone want to watch *Inner Worlds*?

_____

6. Which program gives the national news at 6:30 P.M.?

_____

7. What will you see if you turn to Channel 82 at 7:00 P.M.? _____

8. On which channel can you watch news announcer Sharon Billings? _____

9. Which program appears on Channel 55 first?

_____

10. Which program will show candidates for governor debating?

_____

Synonyms/Antonyms

Synonyms are words that have the same or similar meanings. The words *angry* and *furious* are synonyms. **Antonyms** are words that have opposite or nearly opposite meanings. The words *bright* and *dull* are antonyms. Recognizing synonyms and antonyms will help you learn new words. Try to understand how a word is different from or like a word you know.

A. Choose the synonym for each underlined word in the story. Write the synonym.

delicately	examined	generous	inquire	magnificent	tasty

Daniel carefully (read) _____ the menu. His grandfather suggested that they (ask) _____ about the day's specials. He ordered a (lightly) _____ spiced stew. Daniel began with a (large) _____ serving of soup. Then he ate a crisp, (delicious) _____ salad. The meals were (wonderful) _____!

B. Write the antonym for each underlined word and change the meaning of this story.

pleased	expensive	lightly	sweet
complicated	fresh	small	win

Aunt Jean asked the waiter to describe the special dessert—a (sour) _____ fruit tart. He told her that it was made with (stale) _____ fruit that is (heavily) _____ flavored with honey. Brenda said, "I'm so full, I couldn't even eat a (large) _____ slice of apple." Aunt Jean seemed (annoyed) _____. "Since both our meals are (reasonable) _____, one of us will (lose) _____ the free dessert," she explained. "It is not (simple) _____; I get the dessert."

NAME _____

Vocabulary: Story Critical Words

A. Study the meaning of each word.

dreadful   very unpleasant; terrible
fearfully   with terror or fear
fearsome   causing fear; frightening
grove   a small group of trees

prowling   roaming around in a quiet, secret way
shivered   trembled from fear or cold
thatched   roofed with straw

B. Answer the questions by circling **Yes** or **No.** Each time your answer is **No,** explain why. The first one is done for you.

1. Would you look forward to seeing a <u>dreadful</u> movie?   Yes   No
   A dreadful movie would not be fun to watch.

2. Would a grizzly bear be a <u>fearsome</u> sight to a camper?   Yes   No

   _____

3. Can you cook on a <u>grove</u>?   Yes   No

   _____

4. If you <u>shivered</u>, could you be feeling cold?   Yes   No

   _____

5. Is <u>prowling</u> a sound a lion can make?   Yes   No

   _____

6. Can a scary movie make a person react <u>fearfully</u>?   Yes   No

   _____

7. Can an egg be <u>thatched</u>?   Yes   No

   _____

C. Write the vocabulary word that could describe each of these things.

8. a cat in the neighborhood _____

9. the roof on a 200-year-old house _____

10. a forest fire _____

Vocabulary: Support Words

A. Study the meaning of each word.

brazier   a metal pan for holding burning coals or charcoal
farthest   the most far or distant
haughtily   with too much pride in
  oneself, with scorn for others

ogres   in tales, giants who eat people
panting   gasping; breathing with quick, deep breaths
sympathetically   with understanding of another's
  feelings
trickled   fell in drops; flowed slowly in a thin stream

B. Read the tale. Complete each unfinished sentence with the correct vocabulary word.

The old magician's cabin stood in a distant area. A long time ago, he had built it in

the _____ valley, beyond the eerie swamp. When some villagers

first approached the cabin, they were _____ . Their climb down

the hillside had been hard work. After recovering their breath, two villagers knocked

on the cabin door. They were let into the dimly lit room. There was a log fire burning

in one corner.

''Wise magician, we have come to ask your advice,'' announced the first villager.

''All my neighbors and I are very afraid. We have been told that three very tall

_____ are going to come to our village and steal our children.''

''Ha, ha, there are no such things,'' the old man said _____ .

But when he saw that they were still afraid, he spoke _____ .

''Do you really believe I can fix this problem?'' he asked the villagers.

''Oh, yes!'' they said together.

The old magician then went to the fireplace and carefully picked up the

_____ . He placed it on his workbench and then opened a small

bottle. After saying some strange words and waving his arms around, he tipped the

bottle over the smouldering coals. A silvery liquid _____ out.

''All should be well now,'' said the magician. ''I've done my strongest magic. All

you have to do is believe, and your village will be saved.''

The villagers thanked him very much and began their long journey home.

Synonyms/Antonyms

Synonyms are words that have the same or similar meanings. The words *torn* and *ripped* are synonyms. **Antonyms** are words that have opposite meanings. The words *arrive* and *leave* are antonyms.

A. Write the synonym for the underlined word in each sentence.

awkward	gazed	instruct	pressed	uncertain

1. Lee <u>stared</u> in confusion at the unfamiliar keyboard. _____

2. He was <u>unsure</u> about where to place his fingers. _____

3. Letters appeared when he <u>pushed</u> down on the keys. _____

4. Lee felt terribly <u>clumsy</u> as he sat practicing on the machine.

   _____

5. He hoped that his dad would <u>teach</u> him how to use it. _____

B. Write the antonym for each underlined word.

borrow	excitedly	fascinating	few	shouted

6. Lizette went to the library to <u>return</u> a book. _____

7. While there, she also looked for a <u>boring</u> mystery. _____

8. Lizette found <u>many</u> books that interested her. _____

9. Then she suddenly <u>whispered</u>, "Oh!" _____

10. She <u>calmly</u> held up a book written by an author named Lizette.

    _____

C. On separate paper, write an antonym for the word *uncertain* and a synonym for the word *shout*. Then use each new word in a sentence.

© Silver, Burdett & Ginn Inc.

Characterization

In a story, a character's traits, or special qualities of personality, do not usually change. A character's feelings may change, depending on what happens in the story. Understanding traits and feelings will help you know why characters act the way they do and predict how they will behave.

A. Read the story. Then complete each statement about Mikki.

Mikki raced across the sand. He jumped onto the rocks near the beach. Then he swam gracefully in the cool water. When Mikki came out of the water, he noticed an old milk bottle hidden in the seaweed. Mikki shook the bottle up and down. He tried to peek inside.

Mikki ran over to his sister Tanya. "Hey, look at this! I found a mystery message inside this old bottle!" Mikki knelt in the sand next to Tanya. He imagined that the note was from a distant land.

First Mikki tried to poke a stick into the bottle. He tried to read the faded ink on the paper. But then he gave up and threw the bottle into a trash can. "I'll never get the note out," he muttered sadly to himself as he dropped the old bottle. Then he dashed off to join his sister and their friends in a lively game of beach tag.

1. You find out that Mikki is _____ because he raced across the sand, jumped onto the rocks near the beach, swam gracefully, and played beach tag.

2. You know that Mikki is curious because _____

   _____

   _____ .

3. Mikki gave up on trying to get the note and threw the old bottle into a trash can because he felt _____ .

4. Mikki probably felt _____ when he found the old milk bottle.

5. If Mikki saw a horseshoe crab or a sand dollar on the beach, he would probably

   _____ .

B. Think About Mikki's character traits in the story. Imagine that Mikki finds an old trunk in his grandparents' attic. On separate paper, write three sentences to describe what Mikki might say and do.

Prefixes *in-*, *pre-*, *re-*

A **prefix** is a word part added to the beginning of a word. It changes the meaning of the word.

in- "not" or "in" *inactive,* "not active"
pre- "earlier" or "before" *prewrap,* "wrap before or earlier"
re- "again" or "back" *resell,* "sell again"

A. Read the sentences and decide which prefix is missing. Write the correct prefix. Use the context clues and prefix meanings to help you.

1. Josie looked up at the tree house and blinked, then _____ opened her eyes.

2. The sunlight was shining _____ directly through the spaces between the branches and leaves.

3. To Josie, this old tree looked like a huge _____ historic animal!

4. Her house was beginning to fall apart and needed to be _____ built so that she could continue to use it.

5. Some of the boards had been put together _____ correctly.

6. This time Josie would _____ set them before nailing them together.

7. Also, since the paint was peeling off, she would _____ paint her tree house once it was all fixed.

B. Use your knowledge of prefixes to figure out the meanings of these words. Write their meanings. Use your dictionary for help.

8. incapable _____

9. incomplete _____

10. pregame _____

11. prepasted _____

12. rearrange _____

13. rewind _____

14. input _____

15. regain _____

16. repay _____

17. inaccurate _____

C. On separate paper, write three sentences of your own, using words that have the three prefixes *in-*, *pre-*, and *re-*.

Comparison

An author often compares things to help you understand them better. A **comparison** tells how two or more things are alike and how they are different. Words such as *like, same, unlike, but,* and *also* are sometimes used to signal comparisons. Study the comparison of two types of trees in the example.

> Example: A softwood tree is green all year round, but a hardwood tree is green for only part of the year.

Read the paragraphs. Look for words that signal comparisons. Then answer the questions.

The dodo bird has been extinct, or no longer living, since 1681. The dodo was very large. It looked something like a turkey, only bigger. It had a large bill, and its wings and tail were very small. The dodo bird could not fly or run. It became extinct because of over-hunting and the destruction of its eggs.

The great auk has also been extinct for a long time. The great auk was a large bird. Unlike the dodo bird, it looked something like a penguin. The great auk could swim. Like the dodo bird, however, it could not fly or run. The great auk became extinct because of over-hunting.

1. How were the dodo bird and the great auk different in appearance?

_____

_____

2. In what ways were the dodo bird and the great auk alike?

_____

_____

_____

_____

Drawing Conclusions

A **conclusion** is an idea that goes with the information in a story. It often explains why things have happened in the story. You must think about the story clues and what you already know about things in the story to draw a conclusion.

Story Clues
Experience Clues
Conclusion

+

A. Read each story. Answer the questions and write the story clues that helped you draw the conclusions.

1. Jed and Frankie jumped when the crack and rumble sounded right after a bright flash. Both boys hurried to look out the window. They hoped to see another bright, jagged flash. They forgot about their game of checkers and kept watching the stormy sky. "Wow, this is really wild!" exclaimed Jed.

   What is the weather? _____

   _____

   Story clues: _____

   _____

   _____

2. The small animal with brownish-gray fur hopped quickly across the field. Suddenly it stopped. Its long ears were raised, alert for danger signals. Its powerful hind legs were ready to leap at any moment. If necessary, the animal would dash away to safety.

   What is the animal? _____

   Story clues: _____

   _____

   _____

B. Write what you already knew that helped you draw each of the conclusions.

_____

_____

_____

Vocabulary: Story Critical Words

A. Study the meaning of each word.

betrayed   disappointed because a promise or an agreement was not kept
dignity   proper pride and self-respect
embarrassed   uneasy and nervous about oneself

manager   one who directs the work of others
sewer   a drain that carries off water
spectators   people who watch an event
stranger   a person who is new to a place
ventured   went in spite of some risk

B. Read each row of words. Write the vocabulary word that belongs to the same group.

1. viewers, onlookers, audience, _____

2. president, director, chairperson, _____

3. shy, awkward, ashamed, _____

4. faucet, sink, pipe, _____

5. worth, respect, honor, _____

6. outsider, foreigner, newcomer, _____

C. Answer each question with the correct vocabulary word.

7. Who might explain how to do a job? _____

8. Who might cheer when their favorite team scores a point?

   _____

9. What keeps the street from flooding over after a heavy rain?

   _____

10. How might you feel if someone broke a promise to you?

    _____

11. How might you feel if someone told you that your socks didn't

    match? _____

12. What did the explorers do when they went into unknown territory?

    They _____ .

13. What quality is important to have? _____

Vocabulary: Support Words

A. Study the meaning of each word.

anticipation   the state of looking forward to something; expectation

astounded   greatly surprised

clenched   tightly closed

derisive   making fun of

equipment   special things needed for an activity

fare   money paid for a trip

impressed   affected the mind or feelings

inaccurate   not true

B. Finish each phrase with the vocabulary word that makes the most sense.

1. _____ teeth

2. waiting with _____

3. farm _____

C. Complete each unfinished sentence with the correct vocabulary word.

4. The batter stepped up. She _____ her hands around the bat.

5. Andrew gasped when he received the bill. He was _____ that car repairs could cost so much.

6. On the train, the conductor collected Sam's _____ .

7. Bill improved all his grades. He _____ his parents with his excellent report card.

8. We were counting the days until our camping trip. We looked forward to it with eager _____ .

9. The artist wanted to paint flowers. She set up all her painting _____ in the garden.

10. The waiter made a mistake when he added up the bill. Therefore, the total was _____ .

11. The two politicians could not agree on anything. They made _____ remarks about each other's ideas.

D. On separate paper, write a sentence for each completed phrase in **B** above.

Predicting Outcomes

Often you can guess, or predict, what might happen next as you read a story. When you do this, you are **predicting outcomes.** To make your predictions go with the story, use the story clues and what you know about events like those in the story.

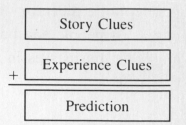

| Story Clues |
| Experience Clues |
| Prediction |

A. Read the story. Write predictions about what will happen.

Gayla and Louis were in their study deck. Soon their parents would be landing the starship on the new planet XT2R. Gayla, who was always ready for adventure, said she could hardly wait to get there. Louis was just as excited, but in a quieter way. He was getting his notebook ready for the notes he would take. He checked three times to see that he had enough paper. Gayla frowned at her brother as she plunked her hands on the table.

1. Prediction: _____

_____

_____

"Oh, Louis," said Gayla. "Why don't you just relax and stop being so fussy about that notebook?"

"I guess you're right," Louis replied. "I wish I were as adventurous as you are!"

As soon as he spoke, they felt the starship land. Louis picked up his notebook. Gayla was already on her way to the exit hatch. After they opened the hatch, they stepped outside. They were greeted by a group of small, friendly looking creatures with very long arms and orange eyes.

2. Prediction: _____

_____

_____

B. On separate paper, write sentences that tell why each of your predictions makes sense with the story.

Telephone Directory

A **telephone directory** helps you locate telephone numbers and addresses. The *white pages* list people and businesses in alphabetical order, according to last name. The *yellow pages* list businesses in alphabetical order, according to the type of business or service they offer.

Read the sample from the yellow pages of a telephone directory. Then answer the questions.

Typewriters — Repairing

Murray Brothers
   148 Dale Dr., Lynn 555-3580

Standard Type Repair
   1250 East St., Lynn 555-3532

Typewriters — Sales and Rentals

North Office Supplies
   36 Curry St., Troy
   Sales 555-8921
   Rentals 555-8922

Town Typewriter Sales
   Name brands — New and Used
   125 Pearl Rd., Lynn 555-3547

Typewriters — Supplies

Total Type
   88 Fay Rd., Troy 555-7700

United Typing Supplies
   29 Cole St., Lynn 555-3586

Typing Services

Lee's Typing Service
   For All Your Typing Needs
   Open Mon.-Fri., 9 a.m.-5 p.m.
   1390 Oak Rd., Troy 555-8614

Pro-Type
   Call anytime
   111 Clarke Ave., Troy 555-6731

---

1. Which heading lists places that would sell ribbons for your typewriter?

_____

2. Which numbers could you call to ask about having your typewriter fixed?

_____

3. Which heading tells you where to buy or rent typewriters?

_____

4. Which companies would you call if you wanted to have a report typed?

_____

5. Who offers used typewriters for sale? _____

6. What number would you call if you wanted to rent a typewriter? _____

Multiple Meanings

A **multiple-meaning word** is a word that has more than one meaning. Notice how *cast* is used in the example.

Example: At the end of the play, the entire *cast* wrote their names on Marcy's arm *cast*.

The word *cast* means "the group of actors in a play." *Cast* also means "a stiff form used to keep a broken arm or leg in place while it is healing."

Complete each sentence by using a word in two different ways. Use context clues to help you.

dull	green	needle	pin	skirt	store	suit	trim

1. As a dressmaker, Kirsten was still _____ , but she wanted to make this _____ cotton outfit herself.

2. She tried not to _____ around any important directions in the _____ pattern.

3. She even read the _____ parts about not using _____ scissors to cut the fabric.

4. Her younger brother began to _____ her while she tried to thread the _____ of her sewing machine.

5. Kirsten wondered if the _____ jacket she was making would really _____ her after all.

6. Before she added lace _____ to the collar, she had to _____ all the loose threads.

7. As she took out the last _____ , Kirsten decided that her star-shaped _____ would look great on the jacket.

8. She planned to _____ her sewing supplies before she went to the _____ for a matching blouse.

Following Directions

In order to follow directions correctly, you must know what steps to take and when to take each one.

A. Write the missing word to complete the directions for how to run a slide projector.

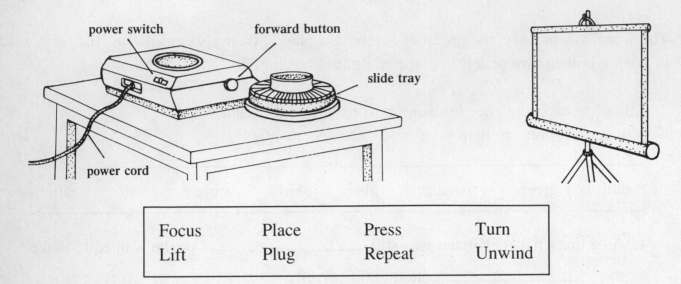

Focus	Place	Press	Turn
Lift	Plug	Repeat	Unwind

How to Run a Slide Projector

1. _____ the slide projector onto a hard tabletop.

2. _____ the power cord from the bottom of the projector.

3. _____ the power cord into the nearest electrical outlet.

4. _____ the round slide tray on top of the projector.

5. _____ the power switch on.

6. _____ the forward button on the projector until the first picture appears on the screen.

7. _____ the first slide until the picture is clear.

8. _____ pushing the button when you want to go on to the next slide.

B. On separate paper, write a list of directions for how to make one of your favorite things to eat, or choose one of these: French toast, grilled cheese sandwich, popcorn, tacos.

Autobiography

An **autobiography** is a person's account of his or her own life. A person might tell about part of his or her own life or all of it. Knowing about what an autobiography is will help you better understand and appreciate this kind of story.

> An **autobiography** is written by an author who tells about his or her own life. A **biography** is written by an author who tells about another person's life.

Read each selection. Then answer the questions.

Selection A

In 1824 a French teenager had a brilliant idea. Louis Braille invented a system for writing and reading. Louis punched groups of dots on paper. The raised dots were part of a code that blind people could easily learn. By using Braille, many people who could not see were given the chance to read and communicate. This system also helped young Louis, who had been blind since the age of three.

Selection B

In the dawn next morning we said goodby to Grandpa and Grandma, to the aunts Mary and Carrie and Grace, who all stood around to watch us go, though Aunt Mary's beautiful blue eyes could not see us. The mares were hitched to the hack; their colts, Little Pet and Prince, would follow them. The Cooleys' covered wagons had gone ahead, and Paul was driving the second one. I climbed up over our wagon's wheel and onto the seat by myself. My mother sat beside me; beside her my father tightened the lines; everyone said, "Goodby, goodby!"

—Laura Ingalls Wilder

1. Who is Selection **A** about? _____

2. Is Selection **A** a biography or an autobiography? Why? _____

_____

3. Does Selection **A** tell part or all of a person's life? _____

4. Is Selection **B** a biography or an autobiography? Why? _____

_____

_____

5. Does Selection **B** tell part or all of a person's life? _____

Vocabulary: Story Critical Words

A. Study the meaning of each word.

contest   a race or game
cupboards   cabinets with shelves for holding
 things
daydreams   pleasant dreamlike thoughts

disappointment   unhappiness felt when
 something wanted did not happen
rhymes   poetry using end sounds that are alike
verses   poems or parts of long poems

B. Answer each riddle with the correct vocabulary word.

1. We can store your food for you until you want to eat it.

   What are we? _____

2. You can win me or lose me, but you should always do your best for me.

   What am I? _____

3. Our ends are not always spelled alike, but they always sound alike.

   What are we? _____

4. Everyone has me at some time, but they get over me.

   What am I? _____

5. When you have us, you can create your own fantasies.

   What are we? _____

C. Some words can be grouped in classes. Read each list of words. Choose the correct title of the class from the box. Write it on the line above the words. The first one has been done for you.

Actions	Decorations	Feelings	Furniture	Magazines	Writings

6. Furniture
   _____
   beds
   tables
   chairs

   _____

7. _____
   sadness
   dissatisfaction
   frustration

   _____

8. _____
   fables
   myths

   _____

   _____

D. Next, choose the vocabulary word that fits each group in **C** above, and add it to the bottom of each list. Note that two vocabulary words fit the third group.

Vocabulary: Support Words

A. Study the meaning of each word.

coasting sliding or riding downhill, as on a sled
guard to take care of; to protect
hedge a row of shrubs or bushes planted together to form a fence

hut a very simple little house or cabin
lane a narrow country road
lean-to a shed with a roof that slopes up and rests against a wall
stringy long and thin like a string

B. Read the story. Complete each unfinished sentence with the correct vocabulary word.

It was a beautiful winter's day, and Marcia and Alfredo decided to go sledding. The sleds had been stored in the _____ connected to the barn. Since they hadn't been used since last winter, their undersides were covered with cobwebs. As Alfredo brushed the sleds, the cobwebs came away in _____ strands.

"All ready to go now," he said. The two children headed immediately down the _____ that led to the big hill.

On their way, they met Jerry and Rosa piling up snow.

"What are you doing?" Marcia and Alfredo asked.

Rosa explained that because the bushes in the _____ were holly, they had to be careful of the thorns when they came sledding down past them. "We're piling snow against the holly to _____ against that danger," said Jerry.

Together the four children quickly finished the task. Then they raced one another to the ranger's _____ on the hilltop. Next, they lined up their sleds, pushed off together, and began _____ down the slope.

C. Read each row of words. Write the vocabulary word that belongs to each group.

1. slipping, sledding, _____

2. shed, cabin, _____

3. street, path, _____

4. secure, shield, preserve, _____

5. barrier, boundary, limit, _____

6. ropy, splintery, wiry, _____

D. On separate paper, write sentences using each of the vocabulary words.

Synonyms/Antonyms

Synonyms are words that have the same or similar meanings.
Antonyms are words that have opposite or nearly opposite meanings.

A. Circle the synonyms in each pair of sentences.

1. Long ago, people drew pictures on clay and stone.
   Their drawings often explained important events.

2. Then paper was created for writing.
   Egyptians made paper from plants.

3. Letters carved into wood were used in ancient China.
   Workers cut thousands of blocks for printing.

4. Later on, printing presses produced finished pages quickly.
   Books and newspapers could be printed rapidly.

B. Circle the antonyms in each pair of sentences.

5. The first comics were just one picture.
   Today, a comic strip shows many pictures in a row.

6. Most modern comic strips are humorous.
   Sometimes cartoons may contain serious messages.

7. In some newspapers, cartoons appear weekly.
   Josh reads the comic strips in the daily paper.

8. The characters in comics might be real.
   Josh likes the imaginary characters best.

C. Underline a word that is either a synonym or an antonym for the first word in each
row. Then write over the word **A** for antonym or **S** for synonym.

9. **false**   answer   blame   question   true

10. **repair**   fix   two   rapidly   repeat

11. **complete**   help   finished   mend   commit

Maps

Maps can vary in type and content. A **political map** shows country and state boundaries, capitals, major cities, oceans, and other major bodies of water. Road maps include major highways and roads, parks, and other points of interest.

Study the map of the British Isles. Then answer the questions.

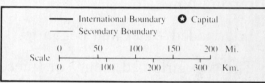

1. Is this map of the British Isles a road map or political map? _____

2. Which two countries share borders with England? _____

3. If you went from Glasgow to Birmingham, in which direction would you travel?

   _____

4. Which capital city shown on this map lies the farthest to the north? _____

5. About how many miles apart are Cardiff, Wales, and London, England?

   _____

6. What country lies to the west of Wales? _____

7. Which body of water would you have to cross to travel from Dublin, Ireland, to Liverpool, England? Circle the correct answer.

   English Channel   Atlantic Ocean   Irish Sea   North Sea

8. Is it the North Channel or the North Sea that lies off the east coast of Scotland?

   _____

Homophones

Homophones are words that are pronounced the same way but have different spellings and different meanings. The words *by* and *buy* and *knight* and *night* are homophones. Recognizing homophones and knowing their meanings helps you understand what you read.

A. Write the correct homophone to complete each sentence. Use context clues to help you choose the best word in each pair.

beet/beat	flower/flour	piece/peace
wait/weight	knead/need	meat/meet

1. Holly put two cups of whole wheat (flower/flour) _____ into a mixing bowl.

2. Fran added water and began to (knead/need) _____ the dough.

3. The two girls had plenty of (piece/peace) _____ and quiet for their project.

4. Holly (beet/beat) _____ the eggs.

5. "What else do we (knead/need) _____ for the pie?" asked Holly.

6. "The recipe calls for one cooked red (beet/beat) _____," said Fran.

7. They also added the sliced (meat/meet) _____ to the bowl.

8. "I wish we could (meat/meet) _____ the person who created this dinner pie," Fran said.

9. When the pie was cooked, Holly said, "Let's try a (piece/peace) _____ right now!"

10. "Let's not (weight/wait) _____," said Fran.

11. Then Fran decorated the top of the pie with a small (flower/flour) _____, and they ate it.

B. Choose one pair of homophones. On separate paper, write two sentences, using a word from the pair in each one.

Context Clues

Sometimes when you read, you will come to a word you do not know. Or, you might come to a familiar word used in a new way. When this happens, use the words and sentences around the word to help you figure out the meaning. This is called **using context clues.**

A. Read the sentences. Use context clues to figure out the meaning of each underlined word. Write the meaning in your own words.

1. Paul sees his uncle <u>frequently</u>. They get together as often as possible.

   _____

2. Paul's uncle likes to do things with other people. He is a good <u>companion</u>.

   _____

3. One day Paul and his Uncle Bill hiked in the country. Paul brought along his <u>canteen</u>, which he had filled with cold water.

   _____

4. They were glad they had it. Their throats felt <u>parched</u> from the hot, dry air.

   _____

5. They stopped to <u>gaze</u> at the mountains. They looked at them as they rested.

   _____

6. They came to what had been a river. All they saw was a dry, flat, dirt <u>bed</u>.

   _____

7. Uncle Bill told Paul a little story about crossing this river once with a donkey. His funny <u>anecdote</u> made Paul laugh.

   _____

8. Paul really enjoyed the hike. He told Uncle Bill how much he <u>appreciated</u> it.

   _____

B. On separate paper, write sentences of your own using each of the underlined words.

Analogies

An **analogy** shows the relationship between pairs of words. Analogies help you learn new word meanings and think carefully.

    Example: *Ax* is to *tool* as *fork* is to *utensil*.

An ax is one kind of tool that is used for chopping wood. In the same way, a fork is one kind of utensil that is used for eating food.

> To complete an analogy, find the link between a pair of the words.

Write the word that correctly completes each analogy.

1. *Skyscraper* is to *city* as *mountain* is to _____ .

          view   country   village

2. *Buckle* is to *belt* as *bulb* is to _____ .

          bright   electric   lamp

3. *Cheerful* is to *happy* as *gloomy* is to _____ .

          smile   sad   cry

4. *Do* is to *did* as *go* is to _____ .

          gone   going   went

5. *Wings* are to *flying* as *legs* are to _____ .

          walking   foot   motion

6. *Teacher* is to *student* as *coach* is to _____ .

          team   player   winning

7. *Wet* is to *dry* as *quiet* is to _____ .

          noisy   damp   whisper

8. *Fifth* is to *sixth* as *ninth* is to _____ .

          order   eighth   tenth

9. *Chapter* is to *book* as *room* is to _____ .

          house   floor   kitchen

Fact/Opinion

Facts are statements that can be checked and proved true or false. **Opinions** are statements that tell what people think or believe that are often supported with facts or examples. Sometimes words and phrases like *I think, I believe, it seems, always, never, probably, might, may, most,* and *best* signal that a statement might be an opinion. Recognizing fact and opinion is important when you read.

Read the example. Notice that the first sentence states a fact that can be proved true or false. *I think* and *best* signal an opinion in the second sentence.

Example: A baseball game will be played at this park tonight.

I think it will be one of the best games ever.

Read the paragraph. Write the sentences that give facts and the opinions. Then underline any opinion signal words in the paragraph.

Good evening, everyone! Tonight the Hampshire Hooters meet the Troy Chiefs. The game is scheduled to start in ten minutes. It will probably be the most exciting game of the season. Tickets are already sold out. In their last game, the Hooters beat the Chiefs 4-3. This game might tell which team is the best.

1. Fact: _____

_____

2. Fact: _____

_____

3. Fact: _____

_____

4. Fact: _____

_____

5. Opinion: _____

_____

6. Opinion: _____

_____

_____

Vocabulary: Story Critical Words

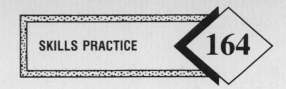

A. Study the meaning of each word.

admired looked at with wonder
complained found fault with something or
 expressed displeasure
declare to say or announce openly
dependable reliable; trustworthy

downcast very unhappy
national relating to the whole country
participate to take part with others in an
 activity
remarkable worth noticing because it is
 unusual

B. Read each row of words. Write the vocabulary word that belongs to the same group.

1. sad, depressed, low, _____

2. fantastic, noteworthy, wonderful, _____

3. public, patriotic, _____

4. reliable, staunch, _____

C. Answer each question with the correct vocabulary word.

5. How might a player feel after helping a team win? _____

6. How might you describe a view of the Grand Canyon? _____

7. What must all the members of a drama club do to put on a play? _____

8. What did the customer do when he returned a faulty product to the

 store? _____

D. The three vocabulary words each describe a type of expression. Write the word
 that describes the style of expression in each quote. Then write your own quote in
 the same style. The first one has been done for you.

admired
complained
declare

9. "Why did the bus have to be so late!" complained
 "I'm tired of hearing that song!"
 _____

10. "That is such a beautiful sculpture!" _____

 _____

11. "I am going to run for class president." _____

 _____

Vocabulary: Support Words

A. Study the meaning of each word.

amount   to add up
disturbed   bothered
errand   a short trip to do a job, usually for
   someone else
event   a happening; any of the contests in a
   sports program

grace   a short prayer giving thanks for
   a meal
integrated   not having people separated by
   their race, color, or religion
partner   one of the owners of a business
sportsmanship   the act of playing fairly and
   not complaining about losing

B. Complete each unfinished sentence with the correct vocabulary word.

1. Ellen went to the store to buy some milk. After she finished this

   _____ , she returned home.

2. Before Thanksgiving dinner, Grandpa said _____

3. The loser of the running race shook the winner's hand. He was showing good

   _____ .

4. Mark could not buy the book he wanted. The money he had with him did not

   _____ to its cost.

5. Mrs. Clark wanted to start a small business. She asked Mr. Alvarez if he would

   like to be her business _____ .

C. The sentences below can be completed with the same vocabulary word. Finish each
sentence by writing the word. Then write the meaning that word has in the sentence.

6. The main _____ of the track meet was the hundred-yard dash.

   Meaning: _____

7. The celebration of the Fourth of July is a national _____ .

   Meaning: _____

D. Write the vocabulary word that is related to each of these words.

8. task _____

9. joined _____

10. interrupted _____

11. companion _____

Connotations/Denotations

The **denotation** of a word is its meaning. The meaning and the feelings or attitudes that people have when they hear a certain word are called its **connotation.** Context clues help you understand the connotation of certain words.

Choose the word that best completes each sentence and write it. Use context clues to help you.

1. Tim finally _____ that he had played the practical joke.

     explained   confessed

2. Anna washed the turnips, made some delicious stuffing, and prepared the

    _____ turkey for roasting.

     plump   overweight

3. "I've lost all my important notes for the science test!" _____ Ken.

     shrieked   exclaimed

4. The nasty little dog's constant barking and yipping _____ the neighbors.

     upset   annoyed

5. Kelly stayed in the waiting room until a doctor could examine the deep

    _____ on her leg.

     cut   scratch

6. All of the children were _____ to go to the park to see the fireworks.

     willing   eager

7. The crowd of fans _____ at the famous movie stars who had just arrived for the awards celebration.

     gazed   looked

8. Bert had to _____ the greasy pots and pans to get them clean.

     scrub   wash

9. The tiny green caterpillar _____ very slowly along the slender twig.

     moved   crawled

Fact/Opinion

A **fact** is a statement that can be checked and proven true or false. An **opinion** is a statement that tells what a person or group thinks or believes. Words and phrases like *I think, I believe, it seems, always, never, probably, might, more, most, all,* and *none* often signal statements of opinion.

A. Read the story. Six of the sentences are facts. Two of the sentences are opinions. Write the facts, and then write the opinions.

> Long ago, books were written by hand. That was probably a very difficult and tiring job. Handwritten books were expensive. In 1440, type was invented. Each letter was on a separate block. The blocks were combined to make words. Soon, many books were printed from type. Some people believe that a very old handwritten book is more beautiful than a printed book.

Fact 1: _____

Fact 2: _____

Fact 3: _____

Fact 4: _____

Fact 5: _____

Fact 6: _____

_____

Opinion 1: _____

_____

_____

Opinion 2: _____

_____

_____

B. Underline the words used in the story that signal statements of opinion.

Analogies

An **analogy** shows the relationship between pairs of words. Read the example.

Example: *Forest* is to *bear* as *pond* is to *frog*.

The first pair of words and the second pair of words are related in the same way. A bear lives in a forest, just as a frog lives in a pond.

> To complete an analogy, find the link between a pair of the words.

A. Write two words to complete each analogy.

field	foggy	nephew	ride	snake	sunny
fish	grass	orchard	slide	snow	uncle

1. *Apple* is to _____ as *corn* is to _____.

2. *Misty* is to _____ as *clear* is to _____.

3. *Aunt* is to _____ as *niece* is to _____.

4. *Cobra* is to _____ as *shark* is to _____.

5. *White* is to _____ as *green* is to _____.

6. *Toboggan* is to _____ as *bicycle* is to _____.

B. Write two words that correctly complete each analogy.

cow	dig	gym	present	swim	today
cut	funny	lion	scared	think	track

7. *Runner* is to _____ as *athlete* is to _____.

8. *Thought* is to _____ as *swam* is to _____.

9. *Cub* is to _____ as *calf* is to _____.

10. *Tomorrow* is to _____ as *future* is to _____.

11. *Shovel* is to _____ as *scissors* is to _____.

Drawing Conclusions

Putting the information an author gives you in a story with what you already know about that kind of information is called **drawing conclusions.** A **conclusion** is a summary statement you can make after reading a story or part of a story.

Story Clues
+	Experience Clues
Prediction

A. Read each paragraph. Write a conclusion to answer the question. Then write the story clues that helped you draw the conclusion.

1. Josh stepped to the edge of the board. He curled his toes over the edge, as if for safety. He wanted to hold his nose, but he knew he shouldn't. He felt fear prickling up and down his bare back. He wasn't sure he could do it, but he'd try!

Where is Josh, and what is he trying to do? _____

_____

_____

Story clues: _____

_____

_____

2. Mrs. Freeman went back to her desk and sat down. After she switched on the machine, she put her fingers on the keyboard. The menu flashed on the screen. She typed in the code, and then pulled up the file. She would finish the report now.

Where is Mrs. Freeman, and what is she doing? _____

_____

Story clues: _____

_____

_____

_____

B. On separate paper, write the experience clues that helped you draw each of the conclusions.

Main Idea/Details

A **main idea** tells what a paragraph is about. **Details** tell about, or support, the main idea. A **topic** is like the main idea except that it is one or two words that tell what the paragraph is about.

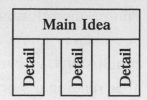

Read each paragraph. Then follow the directions.

Johnny Appleseed planted thousands of apple trees in the Middle West in the late 1700s. He was born in Massachusetts in 1774 as John Chapman. He moved to the Ohio River Valley around 1800. Then he started planting apple tree seedlings all around the area. Johnny Appleseed became a symbol of the westward movement of American civilization. He cultivated as he went.

1. Underline the sentence that states the main idea.

2. Circle the letter of the detail that you would add to this paragraph.

    a. It is not certain whether he had brothers or sisters who moved west also.

    b. He planted the seedlings in what are now Ohio, Indiana, and Illinois.

    c. Many of the people in these areas were successful farmers.

3. Write what the topic of the paragraph is. _____

Thomas Gallaudet was born in Philadelphia in 1787. He became a teacher, and in 1814, he met a child who could not hear or speak. Thomas was sure that young Alice Cogswell could learn to communicate. Thomas began to teach Alice words by pointing to things and printing the words. Before long, Alice could make twenty words with hand gestures! Thomas Gallaudet opened a school for the deaf in 1817. His system is still used today.

4. Circle the letter of the sentence that states the main idea.

    a. Thomas Gallaudet worked very hard as a student and as a teacher.

    b. Thomas Gallaudet taught the deaf in a school in Hartford.

    c. Thomas Gallaudet developed a system of communication for the deaf.

5. Circle the letters of the two details you could add to the paragraph.

    a. Thomas Gallaudet's poor health may have made him physically weak.

    b. His system of communication involved using hand signs to stand for words.

    c. Each position of the fingers stood for a different word or phrase.

Vocabulary: Story Critical Words

A. Study the meaning of each word.

anonymous without a name
asylum a building that shelters people
editorial an article that expresses an opinion

reforms changes for the better
reporter one who writes about events
slums rundown sections of a city

B. One word in each sentence does not make sense. Underline that word. Then write the vocabulary word that belongs in its place.

1. Louis read an interesting editor about the need for more bus routes in the city.

   _____

2. The mayor proposed a plan to rebuild slumps. _____

3. Refunds in the factory made working conditions safer. _____

4. The city decided to add another ward to the assemble. _____

5. The hospital receives many antonym donations. _____

6. The repeater wrote an article about the town elections. _____

C. Write the correct word for each clue.

7. These can make life better for everyone. _____

8. This expresses a particular point of view. _____

9. This person finds out about things that are going on in order to tell the story.

   _____

10. Many people who give to charities like to remain this. _____

D. Complete each analogy with the correct vocabulary word.

11. *Wet* is to *water* as *rundown* is to _____ .

12. *Hospital* is to *doctor* as *newspaper* is to _____ .

13. *Tough* is to *hard* as *unknown* is to _____ .

14. *Seats* are to *chairs* as *improvements* are to _____ .

15. *Book* is to *story* as *newspaper* is to _____ .

Vocabulary: Support Words

A. Study the meaning of each word.

abominable   awful; terrible
circulation   the movement of blood through
  the body
determination   firmness of purpose

insane   mentally ill
lunatic   wildly foolish; insane
workhouses   places where criminals or poor
  people work

B. Write the correct vocabulary word to answer each question.

1. Which two words are synonyms?

   _____   _____

2. Which word is made up of two smaller words? Write the word and draw a line (/)

   between the smaller words. _____

3. Which word refers to a process that keeps people alive? _____

4. *Luna* is the Latin word for *moon*. People once thought the moon made people

   crazy. Which vocabulary word came from the word *luna*?

   _____

C. Finish each sentence with the correct vocabulary word.

5. The flood left the basement in an _____ condition.

6. Doing exercises is good for your _____ .

7. Long ago, people who did not have jobs or enough money to take care of

   themselves sometimes ended up in _____ .

8. Her _____ to succeed never weakened.

D. Look at each word. Place a check mark (✔) beside it if it is spelled correctly. If it is
misspelled, write the word correctly.

9. workhouses _____

10. insain _____

11. determination _____

12. circulation _____

13. abominimable _____

14. lunatick _____

Encyclopedia

An **encyclopedia** consists of several **volumes,** or books. **Guide letters** and **numbers** on the outside spine of each volume help you find the book that contains the information that you need.

An encyclopedia article is a summary of the most important facts about a topic. Articles are arranged in alphabetical order. **Guide words** at the top of each page help you find an article. Articles about people appear in alphabetical order according to last name.

A. Write the number of the volume in which you would find information for each topic. Use the guide letters to help you.

1. Benjamin Franklin —   **5.** ants _____   **9.** China _____

2. electricity _____   **6.** Hoover Dam _____   **10.** bridges _____

3. Coos Bay _____   **7.** geology _____   **11.** Indians _____

4. freon _____   **8.** climate _____   **12.** Denver _____

B. Circle the topics that you would find on these encyclopedia pages. Use the guide words to help you.

13. cats   **18.** cinders   **23.** comet

14. Canada   **19.** chess   **24.** Clearwater

15. cloaks   **20.** Cleveland   **25.** Civil War

16. climate   **21.** cipher   **26.** clouds

17. clams   **22.** clay   **27.** cirrus

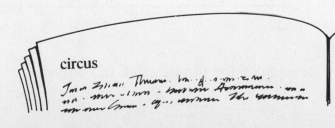

circus

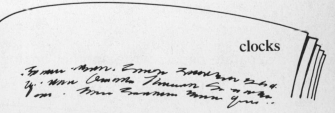

clocks

Analogies

An **analogy** shows a relationship between pairs of words. Analogies help you to build your vocabulary and think clearly.

A. Read each analogy. Then write the phrase that tells how the word pairs are related.

antonyms	the whole and a part
how things feel	times of day
how things taste	units of measure
singular and plural	where actions happen
synonyms	where people work

1. *Face* is to *nose* as *building* is to *door*. _____

2. *Mouse* is to *mice* as *city* is to *cities*. _____

3. *Inch* is to *foot* as *ounce* is to *pound*. _____

4. *Learning* is to *classroom* as *swimming* is to *pool*. _____

5. *Early* is to *morning* as *late* is to *evening*. _____

6. *Last* is to *first* as *quiet* is to *loud*. _____

7. *Chef* is to *kitchen* as *driver* is to *taxi*. _____

8. *Sandpaper* is to *rough* as *velvet* is to *soft*. _____

9. *Plant* is to *stem* as *tree* is to *trunk*. _____

10. *Nurse* is to *hospital* as *teacher* is to *school*. _____

11. *Baseball* is to *park* as *hockey* is to *rink*. _____

12. *Sugar* is to *sweet* as *lemon* is to *sour*. _____

13. *Ham* is to *salty* as *apple* is to *tart*. _____

14. *Cement* is to *hard* as *cotton* is to *soft*. _____

B. On separate paper, write another analogy for each of the phrases that tell ways in which word pairs may be related.

Prefixes *in-, pre-, re-*

A prefix is a word-part added to the beginning of a word. It changes the meaning of the word. Read the meanings of the prefixes *in-, re-, pre-*.

in- ''not'' or ''in''   *informal*, ''not formal''
re- ''again'' or ''back''   *rebuild*, ''build again''
pre- ''earlier'' or ''before''   *prewashed*, ''washed earlier''

A. Write the opposite of these words.

1. formal _____   6. significant _____

2. firm _____   7. sincere _____

3. solvent _____   8. tolerant _____

4. secure _____   9. sensitive _____

5. adequate _____   10. human _____

B. Write these words so that they mean ''do again.''

11. count _____   16. build _____

12. cap _____   17. construct _____

13. adjust _____   18. cover _____

14. fresh _____   19. examine _____

15. write _____   20. discover _____

C. Write these words so that they mean ''earlier.''

21. cancel _____   28. cast _____

22. caution _____   29. occupy _____

23. determine _____ 30. package _____

24. view _____   31. historic _____

25. conceive _____   32. pay _____

26. arrange _____   33. school _____

27. washed _____   34. heat _____

Figurative Language

Writers use **figurative language** to make exact and colorful pictures in the reader's mind. Read the examples of figurative language.

Examples: These grapes taste as sweet as honey. (simile)

My uncombed hair is a bird's nest! (metaphor)

Luckily Bill escaped by the skin of his teeth. (idiom)

"I could sleep for a week!" groaned Kate. (exaggeration)

A. Read the paragraph. Then write a word or phrase to complete each sentence.

blank piece of paper	come up with	mile wide
call it quits	hundred years	tomb

Helen walked into the library. Today it seemed as quiet as an old

(1) _____. Helen knew that she had to

(2) _____ an idea for a report for English class.

Her mind was like a (3) _____. She stared at the

stacks of books. "It will take a (4) _____ to find

an interesting topic!" Helen moaned. But she refused to become discouraged and

(5) _____ on this assignment. Then she saw an

article about cars that run on sunlight instead of gas. Helen was so happy that her

smile was a (6) _____.

B. Draw a line from the first part of the sentence to the ending that goes with it.

7. The scientist's plastic goggles made her look like   throw in the towel.
8. The experiment was so difficult that she was ready to   fall into place.
9. Behind the goggles, her sore eyes were   two burning coals.
10. At first the experiment seemed to   a strange insect.
11. Then, all of a sudden, everything began to   take hours and hours.
12. Completing this experiment was like   winning a big race.

C. On separate paper, write the meanings of these idioms: *call it quits, come up with, throw in the towel, fall into place.*

Vocabulary: Story Critical Words

A. Study the meaning of each word.

console   to comfort; to make less sad

emerged   appeared

gesturing   motioning with one's hands

propelled   pushed or driven forward

reflection   image; anything reflected

sorrow   sadness; grief

unexpected   not expected; surprising

worthy   deserving; good enough for

B. One word in each sentence does not make sense. Underline that word. Then write the vocabulary word that belongs there.

1. The dolphins phoned from the water to jump through the hoop. _____

2. The traffic officer was guessing to the bus driver to stop. _____

3. The loss of Jack's pet caused him great sometime. _____

4. Jo tried to resole his sad friend. _____

5. Mary was not prepared for Carol's unconnected visit. _____

6. The actor's great performance was wordy of an award. _____

7. He studied his deflection in the mirror. _____

8. A small motor repelled the boat. _____

C. Write the vocabulary word that goes with each clue.

9. You see this when you look into a mirror. _____

10. This is what a surprise party is to you. _____

11. This is how an airplane is moved by its jet engines. _____

12. You might do this to someone who is unhappy. _____

13. This is what your work is if you have done your best. _____

14. This is what the mouse did when it came out. _____

15. This has something to do with being kind. _____

16. This is the opposite of "remained still." _____

17. Mimes do a lot of this. _____

18. Prizes are sometimes awarded when one is this. _____

Vocabulary: Support Words

A. Study the meaning of each word.

blackness darkness
cozy warm and comfortable
extraordinary very unusual; remarkable
haltingly hesitatingly; without sureness

marvel to look at with wonder and amazement
monologue a long speech by one person
twilight the dim light just after sunset

B. Read each group of words. Write the vocabulary word that goes with each group.

1. discussion   announcement   dialogue   _____

2. splendid   magnificent   exceptional   _____

3. moonlight   dusk   daylight   _____

4. wonder   gaze   stare   _____

5. soft   pleasant   soothing   _____

C. Write the vocabulary word that could describe each of these things.

6. a view of the Rocky Mountains   _____

7. a soft couch by an open fireplace   _____

8. how a person might ride a bicycle for the first time   _____

D. Finish each sentence with the correct vocabulary word.

9. Kim and Terry _____ at the beautiful pictures that Edie paints.

10. Everyone listened closely to the actor's _____ .

11. The barn was filled with _____ until the farmer lit the lantern.

12. Lou taught his dog to do some _____ tricks.

13. In the _____ , I could barely see the fishing boats out on the lake.

14. We settled down for a quiet _____ afternoon inside the mountain cabin.

Encyclopedia

An **encyclopedia** consists of several **volumes,** or books. On each volume, **numbers** and **guide letters** help you choose a book.

Guide words at the top of each page help you find specific articles.

A. Use the volume numbers and guide letters to answer the questions.

1. Which volume would you use to find information about lions? _____

2. Which volume would give facts about the Statue of Liberty? _____

3. Would you use volume 17 to look for information on these topics? Write **Yes** or **No.**

    a. skiing _____   b. snails _____   c. Spain _____

4. Which volume would have an article about Harriet Tubman? _____

5. Which pair of guide words might appear on two facing pages in volume 21? Circle them.

    a. violin – Virginia   b. walnut – zebra   c. wheat – wheel

B. Circle the topics that might appear on the two pages with these guide words: **Norway** and **octopus.** Then write the topics you chose in alphabetical order.

opera	nylon	oak	New York	nose
numbers	North Pole	ogre	oceans	oats
neighbor	oboe	Ohio	octagons	obelisk

6. _____   9. _____   12. _____

7. _____   10. _____   13. _____

8. _____   11. _____   14. _____

Fact/Opinion

Facts are statements that can be proved true or false. **Opinions** are statements that tell what people think or believe. Sometimes words and phrases like *I think, I believe, it seems, always, never, probably, might, more, most, best, all,* and *none* signal an opinion.

Read the story about koalas (kō ä′ləz). Underline each sentence that gives an opinion. Then write each sentence that states a fact.

The koala is an animal that looks something like a teddy bear. I think koalas are as cute as teddy bears, too. However, they are not really part of the bear family.

Koalas live in the forests in Australia. They spend both day and night in trees. They have strong claws in each of their toes. They probably are not afraid of falling off. They eat the leaves of the trees they live in. It seems as if this diet would be very boring! When a koala is ready to sleep, it curls up on the tree limbs and holds on with its toes. Koalas are the most interesting animals of all.

1. Fact: _____

_____

2. Fact: _____

_____

3. Fact: _____

_____

4. Fact: _____

_____

5. Fact: _____

_____

6. Fact: _____

_____

7. Fact: _____

_____

Newspaper

A **newspaper** tells you about the events happening every day. In a **local newspaper,** the news is mostly about a certain town. A major **daily newspaper** usually reports more national and world news. The **index** in the newspaper will tell you where to find the main sections. Read the newspaper articles and index. Then answer the questions.

The Spillville Times

No. 14 | Spillville, February 11-13 | 20 cents

New Mall Planned for West Spillville

SPILLVILLE   Mayor Riley has announced a new plan to build a modern shopping mall in West Spillville by the spring of next year.

The mall will be built on land near the Mill Falls shoe factory. The site has been empty for two years since the factory closed.

The mayor promises, "This new plan will bring change and growth to Spillville.

There will be many new jobs for workers."

Sanders Construction Company will build the new mall, which is now being planned by Carolyn Ryder. Ms. Ryder said, "The mall will include small shops as well as larger well-known stores."

Index
Comics	D 2
Editorials	A 6-7
Entertainment	C 3-4
News	A 1-5
Sports	B 5-8
Weather	B 2

Storm Rocks Spillville

Spillville residents woke in dark homes Monday. A bad storm had knocked down trees and power lines. Crews worked to clear branches and repair broken lines. Lights came back at 2:15 P.M. Monday.

---

1. Who is the person planning the new shopping mall? _____

2. Who announced the plans for the new mall? _____

3. Where might you find an editorial about the plans for the new mall? _____

4. Which section and page has the cartoon "Silly Spillville?" _____

5. Is *The Spillville Times* a local or a daily newspaper? _____

How do you know? _____

_____

_____

Multiple Meanings

Context clues can help you figure out the meaning of **multiple meaning words.**

Use context clues to write the correct definition of each underlined word.

cart: a small wagon; to carry	**stable:** firm or steady; a place to keep horses
coat: an item of clothing; an animal's fur or hair	**stall:** a section for one animal at a stable; to come to a stop
flock: a group of birds; to come in a group	**stamp:** an official mark; to bring one's foot down heavily
groom: a bridegroom; to brush an animal	
pace: rate of speed while moving; to walk back and forth	

1. George wanted to <u>groom</u> his horse Spice before the show.

<u>Groom</u> means _____ .

2. Spice began to <u>stamp</u> on the ground when she saw him.

<u>Stamp</u> means _____ .

3. George worked until Spice's <u>coat</u> was shiny.

<u>Coat</u> means _____ .

4. He picked up some hay to <u>cart</u> it out of the barn next.

<u>Cart</u> means _____ .

5. Crowds started to <u>flock</u> toward the horse show area.

<u>Flock</u> means _____ .

6. George led Spice out of the <u>stable</u>.

<u>Stable</u> means _____ .

7. He hoped that Spice would not <u>stall</u> at the fence she had to jump.

<u>Stall</u> means _____ .

8. Spice won the blue ribbon for her smooth, steady <u>pace</u>.

<u>Pace</u> means _____ .

Story Elements

The **setting** of a story tells where and when the story takes place. It also introduces the main character. The story may be set in the present, the past, or the future.

Read the story. Then answer the questions about the setting.

Carlo listened attentively to the museum guide. His class was spending Tuesday morning here to learn about how people lived long ago. Their guide pointed to the huge marble statues and explained who the figures were. Then the class gathered around a glass case displaying ancient jewelry and pottery.

After about two hours of seeing exhibits, it was time to go.

"Hey, Carlo! Don't forget your guidebook!" his friend Penny reminded him. After he put on his heavy jacket and wool scarf, Carlo picked up his booklet. Then they all went out the big glass doors into the crisp, frosty air. As Carlo headed for the school bus, he dug into his pocket for his tape player and earphones. He felt like being quiet and listening to music on the ride back to school, while the others chatted about the trip.

1. Where does this story take place? _____

2. Underline the parts of the story that helped you arrive at the answer for question 1.

3. During what season of the year did the story take place? _____

List the details from the story that are clues to the season. _____

_____

4. Which of these phrases tells about when the story takes place? Circle the answer.

Tuesday morning   long ago   about two hours   Saturday

5. Does the story take place in the past, the present, or the future? How do you know?

_____

_____

_____

6. Who is the main character? _____

Vocabulary: Story Critical Words

A. Study the meaning of each word.

allowance   an amount of money

camouflage   coloring that makes a person seem to be part of a landscape

cooperating   working together to get something done

disappointed   unhappy because something expected or desired did not come about

experiment   to test whether a theory is correct

investment   something in which money is put in the hope of making a profit

specialty   something special, such as a product or skill

transformation   a change in form or looks

B. Complete the puzzle by writing the word for each clue.

Across

4. It is good to save this up.

6. A butterfly has gone through this.

7. Savings can add up to this.

8. This allows one to hide.

Down

1. Something done well is this.

2. How a losing team might feel.

3. What a scientist does.

5. Doing this makes work easier.

Vocabulary: Support Words

A. Study the meaning of each word.

assembling   putting together the parts of
encounter   a meeting
introducing   presenting; making known
patchwork   with a design like a quilt sewn
together from pieces of cloth

quivering   shaking; trembling
stern   strict or harsh; not gentle or tender
tentatively   just for the time being; not
for sure
upended   stood or set on end

B. Finish each sentence with the correct vocabulary word.

1. The tiny bird was _____ in the cold.

2. The factory workers were _____ radios and televisions.

3. The space travelers wondered if they would ever have an

_____ with aliens from another planet.

4. The angry man has a _____ look on his face.

5. Bruce _____ the bottle of shampoo to get out the last drops.

6. Stan was _____ Meg to his other friends.

7. Tina's grandmother sewed a _____ robe for her.

C. Answer each question.

8. Which two vocabulary words are made up of two smaller words? Write the vocabulary words. Then draw a line (/) between the two smaller words.

_____   _____

9. Which vocabulary word is an antonym for *definitely*? _____

10. Which vocabulary word is a synonym for *serious*? _____

D. For each group of people or things, write a vocabulary word that tells what each group could be doing.

11. _____ 12. _____ 13. _____

mechanic
toymaker
builder

jelly being carried
hands that are nervous
a tree branch in the wind

speaker talking to an audience
friend talking to two friends
hostess talking to guests

© Silver, Burdett & Ginn Inc.

Prefix *extra-;* Combining Form *mid-*

When a word part is added to a word, it changes the meaning of the word. Read the meanings of *extra-* and *mid-*. Knowing the meanings of these word parts will help you figure out the meanings of some unfamiliar words.

extra- "outside", "beyond"
mid- "halfway", "in the middle of"

A. Write each meaning in the box next to the word it tells about.

> beyond the ordinary
> halfway
> halfway through the winter
> in the middle of the day
> in the middle of the night
> in the middle of a stream

1. midnight: _____

2. midwinter: _____

3. midway: _____

4. extraordinary: _____

5. midday: _____

6. midstream: _____

B. Complete each sentence with one of the words you defined in Part A.

7. Eric stayed up till _____ to welcome in the new year.

8. _____ through the hike, the group stopped for a rest.

9. The sun is highest in the sky at _____ .

10. Everyone agreed that the pure white raccoon was _____ .

11. In _____ , the earth is in a deep freeze.

12. The leaky old boat finally sank in _____ .

© Silver, Burdett & Ginn Inc.

Story Elements

A story's **setting** tells the time and place in which the events happen. It also introduces the main character. Look for clues and details that tell about where and when the story takes place.

Read each passage. Underline the name of the main character. Then answer each question and list details that tell about the setting.

Louisa unhitched the oxen from a plow. The sun began to set over the dry fields. Papa was afraid that they would lose the crops. The summer rains had not come yet, so the ground was hard and dusty. Louisa tried to wipe the dirt off her bonnet and long skirt. Papa would soon be arriving home from Smiley. Just then Louisa heard the rumbling of the old wagon and saw Papa driving the horses. She ran to meet him. After she helped Papa get the horses settled in the old barn, they walked together toward their tiny Nebraska cabin. It was suppertime, and they were both hungry.

1. When does this story take place—in the past, present, or future? _____

Time clues	Place clues
2. _____	**6.** _____
3. _____	**7.** _____
4. _____	**8.** _____
5. _____	**9.** _____

Rafael ran around the track to warm up. An enthusiastic audience in the stadium cheered as the announcement for the race was made over the loudspeaker. This was a major event at these summer games. At exactly 4:05, Rafael crouched at the starting line. Crack! went the signal. He jumped over the hurdles easily and stayed ahead of the others. A television camera crew was there to film his record-breaking finish!

10. When does this story take place? _____

Time clues	Place clues
11. _____	**14.** _____
12. _____	**15.** _____
13. _____	**16.** _____

Predicting Outcomes

When you guess about what will happen next in a story, you are making a **prediction.** A prediction should make sense in the story. Look for clues in the story and think about what you already know about events like those in the story.

Story Clues
Experience Clues
Prediction

+

Read the first part of the story. Write a prediction about what will happen next. Then write clues from the story and experience clues to tell why the prediction makes sense. Finally, check your prediction with the rest of the story.

Meli was new in the neighborhood. She had been invited to a costume party, and she wanted to look good. She wanted her costume to look special, not ordinary. She had an idea and drew a picture. She showed her mother the picture of the kind of costume they could make. Then they went to the store and found the perfect material. It was shiny and silvery.

1. **Prediction:** _____

_____

2. **Story clues:** _____

_____

_____

_____

3. **Experience clues:** _____

_____

_____

_____

Meli and her mother took the material home. Together, they created just the kind of costume Meli wanted for the party.

Synonyms/Antonyms

Synonyms are words that have the same or similar meanings. The words *careful* and *cautious* are synonyms. **Antonyms** are words that have opposite or nearly opposite meanings. The words *fresh* and *stale* are antonyms.

A. Write the pair of synonyms in each sentence.

1. Elena was nervous but knew she would get over her jittery feeling.

   _____

2. She smiled happily and waved cheerfully. _____

3. Elena promised to be a good class president and vowed to work hard.

   _____

4. She made a brief statement and then gave a short speech. _____

5. She explained her new ideas and her plans. _____

B. Write the pair of antonyms in each sentence.

6. Calvin missed the rally but attended the discussion. _____

7. He disagreed with Ted about class rules and agreed with Wanda.

   _____

8. After a noisy beginning, the discussion became quiet. _____

9. When Calvin was asked tough questions, he gave excellent answers.

   _____

10. As Calvin talked, the other students listened carefully. _____

11. Bob seldom went to plays but went often to games. _____

12. She was negative about some things and positive about others.

    _____

13. Jim is a leader; Bill is a follower. _____

14. Although Jim prefers an urban home, he lives in a rural one. _____

15. Some coins were dull, others shiny. _____

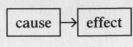

Cause/Effect

An **effect** is what happens. A **cause** is what makes it happen.
Writers sometimes use words and phrases like *because, if, so, since, as a result, such . . . that,* and *therefore* to signal causes and effects.

cause	→	effect

Read the story. Answer the questions about causes and effects.
Then circle the cause-effect signal words in the story.

It was Marisa's mother's birthday, so Marisa wanted to surprise her. Marisa's father suggested cooking her a special dinner. Since they did not have everything they needed, Marisa and her father went shopping for the food. They had such a long list that they decided to split it in half.

When they had finished shopping, they took the groceries to the car. Because there were so many bags, they lowered the rear seat to fit them all in.

As a result of all the shopping, Marisa and her father spent the afternoon cooking. It was all worth it! That night Marisa's mother was very pleased. Therefore, she gave them both a big hug!

1. Why did Marisa want to surprise her mother? _____

2. Why did Marisa and her father go shopping? _____

   _____

3. What was the effect of having a long grocery list? _____

   _____

4. What was the effect of having so many grocery bags? _____

   _____

5. Why did Marisa's mother give them both a big hug? _____

   _____

Vocabulary: Story Critical Words

A. Study the meaning of each word.

enormous   much larger than usual
extraordinary   very unusual
formula   directions for making something

rescue   to free or save from danger
survive   to continue to live
unusual   not common; rare; remarkable

B. Finish each sentence with the correct vocabulary word.

1. Firefighters _____ people from fires.

2. You need special skills to be able to _____ in the wilderness.

3. No one has ever been able to figure out a _____ for making gold.

4. It is _____ to have a lake in the middle of a desert.

5. The Statue of Liberty is _____ .

C. Read each row of words. Write the vocabulary word that belongs or is related to the words in each row.

6. big, huge, _____

7. recipe, instructions, _____

8. uncommon, rare, different _____

9. elephant, hippopotamus, dinosaur, _____

10. fire, flood, danger, _____

11. outlive, outlast, continuing, _____

D. Each vocabulary word in dark print is a describing word. Read the list of items following each word. Put a check mark (✔) beside each item the word could describe.

12. **enormous** _____ a hut _____ a skyscraper _____ an ocean liner

_____ a rowboat _____ a sports stadium _____ an iceberg _____ an ant

13. **unusual** _____ a car with three wheels _____ sand on a beach

_____ a bear in a city _____ a car with four wheels _____ a unicorn

_____ a hot day at the South Pole _____ a hot day at the North Pole

14. **extraordinary** _____ extraterrestrial visitors _____ blue cows

_____ a hot sun _____ a two-headed gorilla _____ a knapsack

Vocabulary: Support Words

A. Study the meaning of each word.

adjusted   changed or moved something to make it fit better

attract   to make come closer; pull towards

digestive   having to do with using food in the body

dimness   darkness, with shadows

miraculous   amazing or wondrous

protecting   guarding against harm or danger

squinted   looked with the eyes partly closed, as in strong light

B. Write the vocabulary word that goes with each clue.

1. Honey will do this to bears. _____

2. Hank did this to his bicycle seat to make it comfortable. _____

3. Lucy did this because it was very bright outside. _____

4. The cat was doing this for her kittens because they could not take care of themselves. _____

5. This could describe a baby learning to walk. _____

6. You would not be able to see easily in this. _____

7. The food you eat goes through this system in your body. _____

C. Complete each unfinished sentence with the correct vocabulary word.

8. Some animals, such as raccoons, stay away from daylight. They like to move in the _____ of night.

9. The bear came out of its dark cave. The animal _____ in the bright daylight.

10. The store manager put up a large, bright "Sale" sign. She wanted to _____ customers into her store.

11. The car's brakes were not working properly. The garage mechanic _____ them.

12. "I'm sorry your stomach is upset," said Dr. Billings. "You have a _____ problem."

Prefix *extra*-;
Combining Form *mid*-

When a word part is added to a word, it changes the meaning of the word.

extra- "outside, beyond"   *extraordinary*, "outside or beyond ordinary"
mid- "halfway, in the middle of"   *midnight*, "halfway through the night" or
                                              "in the middle of the night"

A. Complete each pair of sentences by adding *extra*- or *mid*- to the word in parentheses and writing the new word. Use context clues in the sentences and the word-part meanings to help you.

  1. Mitch wanted to reach the middle of the region by sundown. He was heading to-

  ward the _____ streams.   (land)

  2. It was a hot day in the middle of summer. The _____

  sun beat down.   (summer)

  3. Mitch knew that the heat in the middle of the day was the worst. The

  _____ heat made him thirsty.   (day)

  4. A large bird flew slowly above. It seemed to stop in the middle of the air. It

  looked as if it were stuck in _____ .   (air)

  5. To Mitch, the strange bird seemed to be from somewhere beyond the earth. It

  looked like some kind of _____ being.   (terrestrial)

B. Add *mid*- to one of these words: *stream* or *afternoon*. Use the new word in a sentence about Mitch or the strange bird.

_____

_____

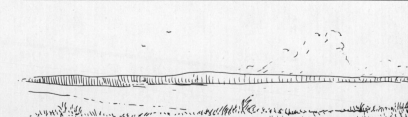

Encyclopedia

When you want information, use an encyclopedia. Each volume has **guide letters** and numbers that help you find the information.

Encyclopedia articles are arranged by topic in alphabetical order. **Guide words** at the top of each page help you find an article. Articles about people appear in alphabetical order by last name.

A. Write the guide letters of the volume you would use to find information for each question.

1. What do giraffes eat? _____

2. Where is Angel Falls? _____

3. Who is Aaron Copland? _____

4. When did Flag Day begin? _____

5. Do anacondas fly? _____

6. Are gremlins real? _____

7. Who was Balboa? _____

8. When is Chinese New Year? _____

9. Where is Iceland? _____

10. Why do bees buzz? _____

11. What causes an echo? _____

12. How do carrots grow? _____

13. Can falcons swim? _____

14. Are elderberries sweet? _____

15. Are grommets metallic? _____

16. Does a dune move? _____

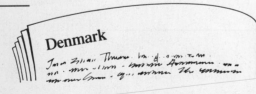

Denmark

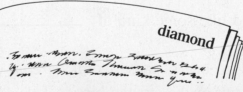

diamond

B. Circle the topics that you would find on these encyclopedia pages. Use the guide words to help you.

17. Denver

18. dentists

19. dinosaur

20. Detroit

21. drama

22. deer

23. dew

24. desert

25. John Dewey

26. Delaware

Reading Rate

The **style** and **rate** of your reading depends on your purpose for reading and on how easy or difficult the material is for you.

A. Read each passage. Time your reading of each passage. Then write the letter of the phrase that best describes your rate and purpose.

a. read faster for entertainment   **b.** read slower for new information

_____ **1.** Every year colorful balloons fill the sky over Albuquerque, New Mexico. The Balloon Fiesta, which is held in October, features a hot-air balloon race. This race is reported to be the largest of its kind in the world. As hundreds of hot-air balloon racers travel along the course, approximately half a million people cheer them on.

Time: _____   New Time: _____

_____ **2.** Tina waited with her father for the balloon to be ready. She held onto the sides of the basket. Suddenly the basket jerked, and the balloon started to rise. Tina's heart beat a little faster. She watched the houses and trees become smaller and smaller. She could hardly believe that she was taking her first hot-air balloon ride!

"How are you doing?" shouted her father. The wind roared.

Time: _____   New Time: _____

_____ **3.** In 1783, Joseph and Jacques Montgolfier made the first hot-air balloon. They used a lightweight material to make the balloon. They heated the air inside the balloon to make it rise. Their giant balloon rose 1,500 feet in the air. It traveled across the French landscape for about ten minutes, landing less than two miles away. Later, the brothers demonstrated their invention for the King of France. This time there were three passengers. A duck, a sheep, and a rooster took the first balloon ride.

Time: _____   New Time: _____

B. 4. Go back and underline key words and phrases, those words and phrases that tell the most important ideas.

5. Now read each passage again and time yourself. Concentrate on the key words and phrases. Write your new time after your first time. Did it change?

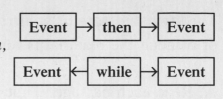
Sequence

In a story, things happen in a certain order, or **sequence.**
Words like *first, second, next, last, finally, after, before, then,*
and *later* signal sequence. Events happening at the same time
may be signaled by the words *while, as,* or *during.*

Event → then → Event

Event ← while → Event

Read the story. Fill in the flow chart with the events in the order in which they
happen. If two events happen at the same time write them in the same box. Then
circle the signal words in the story.

> Jim's older sister Pam was in training for the spring bicycle
> race. On Saturday morning, Pam got up at 7:00 A.M. Her first
> exercises were slow, easy stretches to loosen her muscles. Then
> she did more active exercises for ten minutes. After that, she
> rode her bike for five miles. Back home, Pam ate a good break-
> fast. While eating, she talked to Jim about what exercises she
> would do in the afternoon.

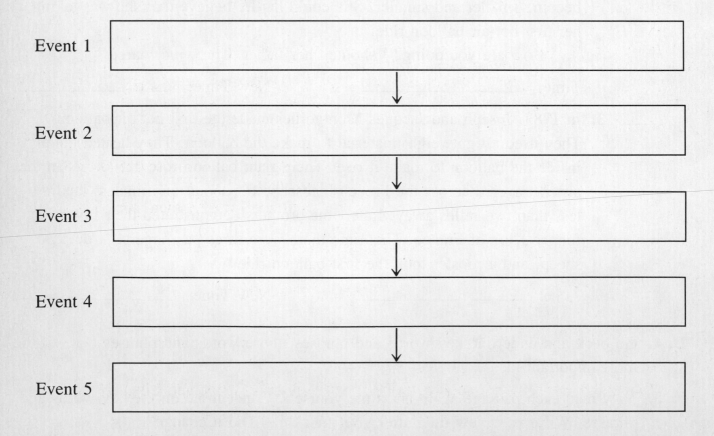

Event 1

Event 2

Event 3

Event 4

Event 5

© Silver, Burdett & Ginn Inc.

Word Referents

Sometimes writers use words that refer to, or stand for, other words. Some of these words are synonyms, or words that mean nearly the same thing. Recognizing these words will help you understand what you read.

Read the example. The word that stands for the circled word is underlined. An arrow goes from the underlined word to the word it stands for.

Example: [Uncle George] is a talented <u>person</u>.

He plays the [violin]. He plays this <u>instrument</u> very well.

[Evening] is his favorite <u>time</u> for playing.

> Also look for pronouns and other words that stand for *people* or *things* or that tell *whose* or *what, where, which one, when,* or *how many.*

A. Read each pair of sentences. Circle the word or words that each underlined word stands for. Then draw an arrow from the underlined word to the circled word.

1. Mike got a puppy last month. His new <u>pet</u> follows him everywhere.

2. Mike named her Lily. One corner of his room is all <u>hers</u>.

3. Lily found a yellow and blue ball. She plays with that <u>toy</u> all the time now.

4. Mike threw the ball under the tree. Then he yelled, "Over <u>there</u>, Lily!"

5. Lily stopped by the daisies. Then she ran around those <u>flowers</u> to get the ball.

6. In the evening Mike walked Lily. She had a wonderful time <u>then</u>, too.

7. Lily was a playful dog. Mike was glad to have an <u>animal</u> of his own.

8. Mike's father likes Lily, too. <u>He</u> thinks <u>she</u> is a great dog.

9. Mike's parents let Lily ride in the car. <u>They</u> say Lily is a part of the family.

B. On separate paper, write another pair of sentences about Mike and Lily. Use a synonym, pronoun, or general word to stand for another word.

Vocabulary: Story Critical Words

A. Study the meaning of each word.

concentrate   to focus one's attention
distribute   to give out in shares
friction   the rubbing of one object against
another
generous   willing to give or share

guardian   a person who guards or protects
intentions   purposes; plans
selfish   caring too much about oneself
tribes   groups of people living together
under a leader

B. Each sentence is incorrect. Rewrite the sentence correctly. Use the underlined word in your sentence.

1. You keep things when you <u>distribute</u> them.

_____

2. A <u>generous</u> person wants to keep everything for himself or herself.

_____

3. <u>Tribes</u> are made up of groups of animals.

_____

4. A <u>selfish</u> person thinks of other people first.

_____

C. Write the correct vocabulary word for each clue.

5. You can study better if you do this. _____

6. This can create heat or a fire. _____

7. This person can be like a parent. _____

8. If you talk loudly in a movie, you may be this. _____

9. Be clear about these before you carry out a plan. _____

10. You share something when you do this. _____

D. Answer the questions.

11. Which two vocabulary words are antonyms of each other?

_____   _____

Vocabulary: Support Words

A. Study the meaning of each word.

amused	entertained	**curiosity**	wanting to know or learn
bonfires	fires built outdoors	**peacefully**	quietly; calmly
colorful	full of color; bright	**sizzling**	having a hissing sound

B. Complete each analogy with the correct vocabulary word.

1. *Soup* is to *bubbling* as *bacon* is to _____.

2. *Boring* is to *interesting* as *dull* is to _____.

3. *Quickly* is to *slowly* as *noisily* is to _____.

4. *Weep* is to *saddened* as *laugh* is to _____.

5. *Owl* is to *wisdom* as *cat* is to _____.

C. Answer each riddle with the correct vocabulary word.

6. We can be made up of dried sticks, logs, and leaves. We can keep you warm.
   What are we? _____

7. If you can't wait to open a present to find out what it is, you know you've
   got me. What am I? _____

D. Answer each question with the correct vocabulary word.

8. What word sounds like the sound it describes? _____

9. What is a synonym for *interest?* _____

10. What word might describe a bowl full of flowers? _____

E. Finish each sentence with the correct vocabulary word.

11. The clown's act _____ the children.

12. After a long day of playing baseball, Ethan slept _____.

13. The autumn leaves created a _____ landscape.

Word Referents

Sometimes writers use words that stand for other words. Some
of these words are synonyms, or words that mean nearly the same
thing. When you read, also watch for pronouns and other
words that stand for *people* or *things* or that tell *whose* or *what,*
where, which one, when, or *how many.*

Read the story. Decide what each underlined word stands for. Write the answer on the
line next to the correct number.

    Jenny and her mother were pulling weeds in the garden.
¹They looked up and saw Roger at the gate.
    "Open ²it and come in," invited Jenny.
    "OK," answered Roger. "That soil looks wet, though. I
don't want to get ³dirt all over my foot cast."
    "Stand on this patch of grass," suggested Jenny's mother.
⁴"It is fairly dry."
    "Look at the beans," exclaimed Roger. "Those ⁵vegetables
are really growing fast!"
    "Yes," answered Jenny. "And look at the size of the toma-
toes. ⁶Those are growing well, too."
    Jenny's mother pointed to the end of the garden. "We have
watermelons growing over ⁷there," she said. ⁸"I started to grow
⁹them last year."
    "That ¹⁰fruit is juicy and fun to eat!" exclaimed Roger. ¹¹"I
can hardly wait! The tomatoes look great too. When can we
pick ¹²them?"

1. They _____

2. it _____

3. dirt _____

4. It _____

5. vegetables _____

6. Those _____

7. there _____

8. I _____

9. them _____

10. fruit _____

11. I _____

12. them _____

Story Elements

A story **setting** tells where and when the story takes place. It also introduces the main character. Knowing the setting of a story helps you understand its characters and events.

A. Read each passage. Circle the name of the main character. Write a sentence to tell when the story takes place—in the past, the present, or the future. Then write the details from the story that you used as clues.

Kren anxiously boarded the Venus Ferry. Her wrist counter showed that they had just passed the twelfth revolution of the planet. Kren thought about the new phraser she wanted to give to her cousin Larka. "How many milliseconds will it take to get to Venus?" she asked the captain.

"It should take about 20 milliseconds once we leave Ord," said Captain Jollo. "We are just waiting until we receive word that the solar flares of the sun will give us the transport power we need to sail for home."

1. Time: _____

2. Story clues: _____

_____

_____

King Elwin stood at the edge of the castle wall and searched the horizon. He saw the tiny figure of a knight on horseback in the distance. He hoped that Lars the Swift would have good news. King Elwin knew that his brother, the Knight of Elred, was marching with his followers to take over tiny Bostphia. And now, the only person who could save the kingdom was Lars the Swift.

"My king, I have found the magical fog you wanted," called out Lars. "It will cover all of Bostphia and make it invisible for a time. Soon not a trace of our kingdom will be found. Your brother Elred has been fooled."

3. Time: _____

4. Story clues: _____

_____

_____

B. Underline the words in each passage that tell the place, or *where*, the story is set.

Comparison

Writers often tell how two or more things are alike or different. Words such as *alike, like, both, same, different, unlike, but,* and *whereas* are sometimes used to signal **comparisons.**

Read the paragraphs about two kinds of bears. Then write in the chart how they are alike or different. Finally, circle the signal words in the paragraphs.

Polar bears are large, white bears. They live by the seacoasts near the North Pole. Polar bears are good swimmers. They hunt on the ice for fish, seals, and walruses. In the summer they may go inland and eat grasses or other plants. Polar bears are about eight feet long, and they weigh about one-half ton.

Kodiak bears are the biggest bears in the world. Unlike polar bears, Kodiak bears are a yellow-brown color. They live along seacoasts and on islands in Alaska and Canada. Whereas polar bears can swim far, Kodiak bears stay on land or in shallow water. They like to eat fish, especially the salmon that they catch in streams. They also eat plants, insects, roots, and mice. Once in a while they eat animal meat. These big bears grow to nine feet long, and they weigh about three quarters of a ton.

	Polar Bears	**Kodiak Bears**
1. Where They Live	_____ _____	_____ _____
2. Color	_____	_____
3. Length and Weight	_____ _____	_____ _____
4. What They Eat	_____ _____ _____	_____ _____ _____
5. Where They Hunt	_____	_____

Dictionary

A **dictionary** contains entries listed alphabetically. Each **entry** tells what the entry word means and how to say it. Other forms of the word appear at the end of the entry. To help you find a word quickly, use the **guide words** at the top of each page.

Read the sample dictionary page.

---

ice/idle

ice (īs) *noun* **1.** frozen water. **2.** a frozen dessert, usually made of water, fruit juice, egg white, and sugar. *verb* **1.** to freeze. **2.** to fill with ice **3.** to cover with frosting. —**iced, icing**

icicle (ī′si k′l) *noun* a stick of hanging ice formed by dripping water.

PRONUNCIATION KEY

a	fat	ī	bite, fire	σu	out	zh	leisure
ā	ape	o	cob	u	up	nĝ	ring
ä	car, lot	o	hop	ur	fur	a	*in* ago
e	ten	ō	go	ch	chin	e	*in* agent
er	care	ô	law, horn	sh	she	ə =	i *in* unity
ē	even	σl	oil	th	thin	o	*in* collect
i	hit	σo	look	*th*	then	u	*in* focus
ir	here	σ̄o	tool				

icy (ī′sē) *adjective* **1.** covered with ice. **2.** slippery; very cold. **3.** unfriendly. —**icier, iciest** —**icily** *adverb*

idea (ī dē′ə) *noun* **1.** what someone thinks, believes, knows, feels. **2.** a plan.

ideal (ī dē′əl) *adjective.* **1.** perfect. **2.** imaginary. *noun* **1.** a standard of perfection. **2.** a perfect model.

ideally *adverb*

idle (ī′d′l) *adjective* **1.** not busy. **2.** lazy. **3.** worthless. —**idler, idlest.** *verb* **1.** to spend time doing nothing. **2.** to run slowly. —**idled, idling** —**idleness** *noun*

A. Use the guide words to circle the entry words that would appear on this dictionary page.

1. ignore   **3.** ill   **5.** igloo   **7.** Idaho   **9.** ice skate

2. iceberg   **4.** if   **6.** iceboat   **8.** imagine   **10.** Iceland

B. Read each sentence. Then write the number of the correct meaning of the underlined word.

11. Mr. Field gave us an <u>icy</u> stare. _____

12. The mayor shared her <u>idea</u> for the new park. _____

13. Try not to slip on the <u>ice</u>. _____

14. Maria ate a delicious strawberry <u>ice</u>. _____

Fact/Opinion

Facts are statements that can be proved true or false. **Opinions** are statements that tell what people think or believe. Words and phrases that often signal a statement of opinion include: *I think, I believe, it seems, always, never, probably, might, may, more, most, best, all,* and *none*.

A. Read the article announcing a carnival. Underline the facts. Then write the opinions.

May 21st is the most exciting day this spring! That is the day Johnson Elementary School is holding its 5th Annual Outdoor Carnival. There are over 50 prizes to win at the ten game booths. The prizes were made by Johnson Elementary School students. I think the prizes are great!

There will also be food tables. The food will be made by parents of the students. Mr. Grimley's special Dutch apple pie with raisins will probably be the most tasty dish at the carnival.

The money from the carnival will be given to the Kids for Arts School. It may be the most wonderful school around. It helps children who want to learn about the different forms of art. The use of the proceeds to help this school is a great idea.

1. Opinion: _____

_____

2. Opinion: _____

_____

3. Opinion: _____

_____

4. Opinion: _____

_____

5. Opinion: _____

_____

B. Look again at each sentence you wrote and circle the words that signal an opinion. On separate paper, write one statement of fact and one of opinion that will go with this passage.

Vocabulary: Story Critical Words

A. Study the meaning of each word.

barefoot without shoes
career the way one earns a living
championship first place
contract an agreement
permission consent; the act of allowing

soccer a game in which a ball is moved by kicking
tournament in medieval times, a contest of knights; a group of games
victor the winner in a contest, struggle, or battle

B. Finish each phrase with the vocabulary word that makes the most sense. Then write a sentence using that phrase. The first one is done for you.

1. be the ___victor___ : ___Who will be the victor of this game?___
   _____

2. sign a _____ : _____
   _____

3. play a _____ game: _____
   _____

4. give _____ : _____
   _____

5. win a _____ : _____
   _____

6. go for a _____ walk: _____
   _____

C. Read each row of words. Draw a line under the word that does not belong in the row. Write the vocabulary word that does belong.

7. basketball singing gymnastics _____

8. hobby job work _____

9. agreement deal invitation _____

10. games careers races _____

Vocabulary: Support Words

A. Study the meaning of each word.

competition   a contest
dribbling   controlling the ball while moving, as in basketball or soccer
enthusiasm   a strong liking or interest
exhibition   a display for the public
goal   a score made by getting a ball into a net

league   groups joined together for a common purpose
pray   to ask seriously for something
uniforms   special clothes worn by members of certain groups

B. Read the story. Complete each unfinished sentence with the correct vocabulary word.

Effie and Billie Jo had worked hard to start a soccer team. They had even designed

_____ for their team to wear. The team had practiced every afternoon.

Now the players were ready to compete in the girls soccer _____ of

their area.

The first game of the season was about to start. All the players were excited and

showed a lot of _____ . This game was part of a big sports

_____ at the state's largest stadium. Many people were there to see

who would win the _____ that day.

Billie Jo and Effie ran onto the field with their team.

"This game is so important. I _____ that all our practice pays

off," Effie said.

"We'll soon find out," replied Billie Jo. "At any rate, I'm sure it will be fun."

Their team seemed a little nervous at first. But as they began kicking and

_____ the ball during their warm up, they relaxed.

The spectators cheered throughout the game. Then when there were only five

minutes of playing time left, the crowd began to roar. The score was an even 2 to 2.

Now the teams struggled hard to score the winning _____ .

© Silver, Burdett & Ginn Inc.

Word Referents

Sometimes writers use words that stand for other words. Some of these words are synonyms, or words that mean nearly the same thing. Read the example. Notice that the underlined word refers to the word that is circled. An arrow goes from the more general word to the word it stands for.

Examples: Mrs. McDell raises ⬡sheep.⬡ She takes good care of the <u>animals</u>.

They graze in nearby ⬡hills.⬡ The grass <u>there</u> is good for them.

> Look for words that stand for *people* or *things* or that tell *whose* or *what, where, which one, when,* or *how many.*

A. Read the sentences about opossums. Circle the word or words that each underlined word stands for. Then draw an arrow from the underlined word to the word or words you circled.

1. Opossums have long fur. These <u>animals</u> also have long, bare tails.

2. Most opossums are about two feet long. A <u>few</u> are only six inches long.

3. Opossums eat insects. They hunt for this <u>food</u> at night.

4. During the day, opossums are found in burrows. They sleep in these <u>holes</u>.

5. Opossums move easily throughout tree tops. <u>Some</u> that live in South America can even swim.

6. When surprised, an opossum often plays dead. <u>It</u> fools its enemies that way.

7. Baby opossums are only one-half inch long. These young <u>animals</u> need their mother's protection.

8. Opossum mothers carry their young in pouches. They are carried <u>there</u> for months.

B. On separate paper, write a pair of sentences about a pet or wild animal you are familiar with. Use a synonym, pronoun, or general word to stand for another word.

Prefix *extra-*;
Combining Form *mid-*

When a word part is added to a word, it changes the meaning of the word.

extra- "outside", "beyond"   *extracurricular,* "outside the regular course of study"
mid-   "halfway", "in the middle of" *midstream,*   "in the middle of the stream"

A. Read the sentences. Write a definition for each underlined word. Use meaning clues in the sentences and the word-part definitions to help you.

1. Ms. Sanchez came into class right after lunch. She gave her talk at <u>midday</u>.

   _____

2. She had traveled to Mexico on her winter vacation. So she told the class all about her <u>midwinter</u> trip.

   _____

3. She had gone on a canoe trip. One time, her canoe got stuck on a rock <u>midstream</u>.

   _____

4. She had some other unusual adventures also. Her entire trip was <u>extraordinary</u>.

   _____

5. <u>Midway</u> through her talk, Ms. Sanchez showed pictures of her trip.

   _____

6. Ms. Sanchez planned another trip to Mexico for the <u>midterm</u> break, in the spring.

   _____

B. Write sentences. Use each of these words in a sentence: *extraterrestrial, midyear, midair, midday.*

_____

_____

_____

© Silver, Burdett & Ginn Inc.

Connotations/Denotations

The **denotation** of a word is the dictionary meaning of the word. The **connotation** of a word is the meaning and the feelings that most people have when they hear the word. In the example, the underlined words have similar meanings but different connotations.

Examples: The <u>fog</u> made our drive difficult.
A cool <u>mist</u> settled over the lake.

Answer each question by writing one of the underlined words.

1. Is the Grand Canyon <u>large</u> or <u>immense</u>? _____

2. Does a fire alarm <u>clang</u> or <u>ring</u>? _____

3. Would it be better to have <u>wet</u> or <u>soggy</u> boots? _____

4. If you slipped, would you <u>clutch</u> or <u>hold</u> a railing? _____

5. Should you <u>slam</u> or <u>shut</u> a door? _____

6. Would you rather feel <u>full</u> or <u>stuffed</u> after dinner? _____

7. Which is easier to do, a <u>chore</u> or a <u>task</u>? _____

8. Is it a <u>journey</u> or a <u>trip</u> when someone goes to the store? _____

9. Do you prefer <u>warm</u> or <u>humid</u> summer days? _____

10. Do flags <u>wave</u> or <u>move</u> in the wind? _____

11. Do very thirsty horses <u>sip</u> or <u>gulp</u> water? _____

12. Is it healthier to be <u>thin</u> or <u>skinny</u>? _____

13. Would you rather hear <u>funny</u> or <u>silly</u> jokes? _____

14. Would you rather eat <u>soft</u> or <u>mushy</u> peaches? _____

15. Is it more polite to <u>argue</u> or <u>discuss</u> differences? _____

16. Which might bother you more, a <u>shrill</u> or a <u>loud</u> voice? _____

17. Does a boulder <u>tumble</u> or <u>crash</u> down a mountain? _____

18. Do you <u>push</u> or <u>shove</u> a lawn mower? _____

Characterization

A character's **traits** are special qualities of personality. A character's traits usually do not change a story, yet the character's feelings may change, depending on what happens.

A. Read the story. Then answer the questions.

When he was only fifteen, Chester Greenwood solved the problem of cold ears. He invented earmuffs. His idea helped people in the winter.

Chester explained his idea to Grandmother. She smiled and nodded as he described his plan. She told him that she thought he was some kind of genius, and of course she'd help him!

First Grandmother bent some wire into two circles. She sewed fur onto one side of a circle and velvet on the other side. Then she repeated these steps with the second wire circle. She connected both circles with wire.

She had followed Chester's directions exactly to help her grandson with his project. Now Grandmother proudly gave him the earmuffs.

"Oh, Grandmother!" exclaimed Chester. "Now my ears will be warm when I ice-skate. Will you make a pair for Billy, too?"

1. Which sentence tells how Grandmother felt after Chester described his plan?

_____

Grandmother seemed annoyed by Chester's plan.
Grandmother was delighted with Chester's plan.

2. What might Grandmother have said to Chester?

_____

"I have too many chores to do, Chester."
"I would love to help you, Chester."

3. How did Grandmother show that she could be counted on to help?

_____

Grandmother followed each step in the right order.
Grandmother designed her own set of earmuffs.

B. Go back into the story. Underline words and phrases that give clues to Grandmother's character traits.

Comprehension Monitoring

When you read, you should ask yourself often, "Does this sentence or story make sense?" If something does not make sense, you will need to read it again or do something else so that you understand better. Figure out why the example sentence does not make sense. If you replace the word *refrigerator* with the word *leaves* would it make sense?

Example: The refrigerators fell from the autumn trees.

A. Read each story. Some words do not make sense. Underline each of those words. Then write a word from the box that does make sense.

bench	build	homes	left	lost	piano	play	swings
books	drove	journey	longest	moved	pictures	snow	years

1. It was the first day of school. The bus driver swam to the first stop. Two boys carrying kangaroos got on and took seats together.

_____
_____

2. Trudy started taking lemonade lessons last week. She practices scales every day, and now she can sleep three different songs.

_____
_____

3. Paco has lived on Madison Street for three puddles. Erica and Nathan just lizard there last month. Paco has been there the shortest.

_____
_____
_____

4. Karen and her mother sat on a jungle and ate a picnic lunch. Then Karen rode on the flute, and her mother took gum with her camera.

_____
_____
_____

5. The pioneers had a long and difficult orchestra. They had outlined many friends behind. They felt it would be worth it, though, to find new needles.

_____
_____
_____

6. The newly-fallen mushrooms sparkled in the sun. Corey ran outside to burn a snow house. He played so hard he mailed one of his mittens.

_____
_____
_____

Comprehension Monitoring

B. Read each story. In each, some sentences do not fit or make sense. Underline them. Then reread each story to make sure you found all the sentences that do not fit.

7. Megan went to the museum with her aunt. First her aunt bought tickets at the door. Then they gathered beautiful sea shells. Next, they decided which display to see first. They decided to see the "Ancient Skies" display. There, they saw pictures of the stars as people of the past had viewed them. The sky is often full of clouds in March. Then Megan's aunt said she would like to see the "Sea Travel" display. Mr. Godfrey's boat would be launched next week. At that display, they saw models of reed boats, old fighting ships, and modern tankers. By that time, Megan and her aunt were quite tired. They ran around the block. Then they went home.

8. The fourth-grade class is having a "History of America" fair next week. Parents and friends are invited. Two out of every three pupils have a pet. There will be three booths at the fair. Nadine is staying overnight at Josie's house. Each child will make something for one of the booths. One booth is about the Pilgrims who settled in America. People eat corn in many different forms. Tomi, Erica, Nathan and Steve will sew small costumes to show how the Pilgrims used to dress. Steve's new puppy is called Quilt. The second booth is about the Indians of early America. David and Muna will write the story of Squanto and draw pictures to go with it. Knowing just where to catch the best fish is important. The third booth is about different foods grown and eaten in early America. Plantation slaves in the South were not free. Miya and Juan will draw pictures of early farms. Cassie and Lucas will bake corn bread with Mrs. Freeman. Her cousin lives in Michigan. Everyone expects the fair to be a huge success.

9. Marlene has a new kitten. The first day she had him, he fell into the sink where Marlene's mother was washing her hands. They decided to call the kitten Suds. Marlene's mother is a supervisor in a bank. That night, Suds cuddled up next to his new owner and slept with her all night. Marlene awoke the next morning to the sounds of loud purring. Suds once skied down the side of a mountain. When she got out of bed, Suds followed her everywhere. Marlene went into the kitchen. Then she rode on a train. Suds was right at her heels. Then she realized that the little kitten was hungry. She hit the ball back across the net. When Marlene opened a can of cat food, Suds gave out three loud meows. Marlene's mother was in the living room. Marlene is very glad that Suds is her kitten, even if he is a little pesky.

Visualization

When you read, you can draw a picture in your mind of what you are reading. For example, read the paragraph about Mona's costume. Can you picture in your mind what the costume looks like?

Mona was dressed as a magician. She had a tall, pointed hat made of dark blue satin. It had shiny stars all over it. Her cape was made of the same material, but it had shiny silver and gold stars all over it. She wore a wide, red satin sash. In her hand, she held a wand with a star on the end of it. Her boots were black and shiny and had laces.

A. Read the description of Terri's aunt's house. Make a picture of the house in your mind. Then draw a picture of it.

1. All of Terri's friends love to visit her aunt's house in the country. When you ride up the curved driveway, the first thing to catch your eye is the front porch that runs along the whole front of the house. There are always four or five folding chairs on the porch, and often Terri's aunt is sitting in one of them. In front of the long porch is a row of rose bushes. There are red, white, and peach colored roses on those bushes, and they are huge! There are also deep green vines trailing in and out of the slats on the railing going up the three steps and along the porch. The front door of the big white house is painted a deep red, and it seems to say "Come in." On the door is hung a straw basket that Terri's aunt uses as a mailbox. There is often a hot pie cooling in one of the open front windows. It is a great place!

Visualization

B. Read this letter from Robert to his pen pal Michelle in France. Robert is describing a photograph he is sending along. The photograph shows Robert's family at his tenth-birthday cookout. Make a picture in your mind of the photograph. Then draw a picture of it without looking back at the letter. When you are finished drawing, look back at the letter to see if you have left anything out of your picture.

2. Dear Michelle,

    Here is a picture of my tenth-birthday cookout. Right in the middle of the back yard you can see a large picnic table with birthday balloons and other decorations. To one side of the table is my older sister, Sharon. She has on Dad's cooking apron, and she is cooking chicken on the grill. In front of the table, Mom and Dad are holding my birthday cake that has "Happy Birthday, Robert" written on it. To their right, waving, is my younger brother, Randy. To their left, in Randy's red wagon, is my dog Huff. He has a bone in his mouth and a bow around his neck. Joining him in the wagon is the neighbor's multicolored cat, Elton. Hope this makes you feel that you were at the party too.

                          Sincerely,
                          Robert

Comprehending Relationships

Questions that can be answered by using the words right from the story are called **memory questions.**

> These words can help you form questions: **who, what, when, where, why, how.**

A. Read the paragraph about sea urchins. Then read the memory questions.

   Sea urchins (ur′ chinz) are small animals with hard shells that live on the ocean floor. They have a round shape, with many long spines sticking out of their shells. Sea urchins use these spines as legs, for moving. Between their spines, they have small organs that look like claws. They use these for cleaning and to defend themselves against enemies. Sea urchins eat plants and small animals. You would not want to step on a sea urchin because it is poisonous, and its spines are sharp.

What are sea urchins?   Where do they live?

B. Now write six more memory questions about the paragraph. Use the words *what, where, why,* and *how* in your questions. Be sure that the answers to the questions are right in the paragraph.

   1. _____

   2. _____

   3. _____

   4. _____

   5. _____

   6. _____

C. Choose four of your questions and write the answers to them.

   7. _____

   8. _____

   9. _____

   10. _____

Comprehending Relationships

D. Read this passage about Sacajawea (sak ə jə wē′ə). Ask memory questions about the passage. Use the question words in your questions.

Sacajawea was a Shoshoni woman. Although she was Shoshoni, she had not lived with her people for a while. In the early 1800s, she was living in the area of North Dakota.

11. **Who** _____

12. **Where** _____

13. **When** _____

It was in 1804 that the American explorers, Lewis and Clark, met Sacajawea. They found out that she knew a lot about the Rocky Mountain area. She also could speak the Shoshoni language. Lewis and Clark needed a guide with these abilities to help them get across the Rocky Mountains, so they asked Sacajawea to be their guide.

14. **What** _____

15. **Why** _____

Sacajawea had not seen her people, the Shoshoni, for a long time. They lived in the Rocky Mountain regions that Lewis and Clark wanted to explore. Therefore, Sacajawea agreed to go along as their guide and visit her people again.

16. **Why** _____

The expedition faced special dangers as they traveled in the Rocky Mountains. The traveling was difficult, and there were many rattlesnakes and grizzly bears along the way.

17. **What** _____

Sacajawea did successfully guide Lewis and Clark in the mountain regions. They eventually arrived safely in the land of her people, the Shoshoni.

18. **Where** _____

There, the Shoshoni sold Lewis and Clark some horses. They also told them the best way to continue on their journey through the Rockies.

19. **How** _____

Non-Technical
FORTRAN

Non-Technical FORTRAN

PRENTICE-HALL, INC., Englewood Cliffs, New Jersey

ata

e) I. Title.

-Hall, Inc. Englewood Cliffs, N. J.

10 9 8 7 6 5 4 3 2 1

Printed in the United States of America

PRENTICE-HALL INTERNATIONAL, INC., *London*
PRENTICE-HALL OF AUSTRALIA, PTY, LTD., *Sydney*
PRENTICE-HALL OF CANADA, LTD., *Toronto*
PRENTICE-HALL OF INDIA PRIVATE LIMITED, *New Delhi*
PRENTICE-HALL OF JAPAN, INC., *Tokyo*
PRENTICE-HALL OF SOUTHEAST ASIA (PTE.) LTD., *Singapore*